Molecular
Control
of
Plant Growth

Dickenson Series on Contemporary Thought in Biologicial Science

Elof Axel Carlson/Consulting Editor

Bruce H. Carpenter	Molecular and Cell Biology
Edward Glassman	Molecular Approaches to Psychobiology
Elof A. Carlson	Gene Theory
J. Richard Whittaker	Cellular Differentation
Arthur S. Boughey	Population and Environmental Biology
J. Eugene Fox	Molecular Control of Plant Growth
Rodolfo Ruibal	The Adaptations of Organisms

J. Eugene Fox / Molecular

The University of Kansas

Control

43

of

Plant Growth

Dickenson Publishing Company, Inc., Belmont, California

Contemporary Thought in Biological Science

Advances in the biological sciences occur with such a rapidity that the traditional textbook is often out of date before it reaches the student. Furthermore, new contributions to biology are distributed among hundreds of technical journals. Neither the teacher nor the student can cope with this immense and scattered mass of knowledge.

The paperback volumes in this series on Contemporary Thought in Biological Science serve several purposes. Each volume presents a selection of key or illustrative papers in a current field of biology. The editors hope that their selections will stimulate the teacher and the student to increase their awareness of the new advances in biology. Through the teacher's guidance the student may appreciate some of the experimental design and ideas which the research worker presents in his technical publications. Although some of the readings may be difficult and uneven, each article was chosen carefully because of its outstanding illustration of new ideas.

The exposure, in undergraduate courses in biology, to the original articles from which lectures are prepared will also give the student an insight into the creative imagination that the teacher must use to convey these scientific advances to his classes. This series also offers an experimental and flexible approach to teaching biology. New fields may be interdepartmental, and the diversity of concepts which constitute a new segment of knowledge may seem unrelated at first, but in reading these selections the student soon recognizes that these separate contributions lead to a pattern recognizable as a whole. It is this diversity of knowledge and opinion, communicating the excitement of contemporary biological thought, that each volume attempts to convey.

Elof Axel Carlson

Preface

The growth of higher plants is regulated by a precise and delicate interaction of the environment together with a few, fairly simple chemical substances within the plants themselves. Our knowledge of at least one group of these substances, the auxins, dates back more than forty years and has been based upon hundreds of research papers describing the involvement of the auxins in nearly every phase of plant life. Despite this vast literature almost nothing is known about the machanism of action of these or other substances controlling form and function in the plant.

In the past few years, however, the advances in technique and instrumentation which have made possible great strides in the molecular biology of microorganisms have been carried over to plant biology. As a consequence there are now just beginning to appear exciting research reports which lead one to believe that we may be close to discovering how the plant hormones control growth and development. It comes as no surprise to find that many of the readings in this volume implicate the plant growth substances at the polynucleotide level. For substances with the diverse activities of, for example, indoleacetic acid—the auxin that plays a key role in cell elongation, seed germination, flowering, fruiting, leaf abscission, and other important plant growth processes—one would scarcely expect otherwise.

In a field that has developed as recently as this one, it is not possible to speak of "classic" papers. The readings in this collection were chosen only to represent "hot" areas that are developing in plant biology and are not necessarily the first nor the most detailed reports. The oldest paper was published little more than ten years ago and the majority of the papers less than five. The fact that these reports are so little removed from an advancing research front makes it all great fun for the reader who may be able to spot conclusions that become faulty or outdated as new information is obtained. It is hoped, therefore, that this collection will stimulate the reader to go to the current literature so that he can reread these papers with a properly critical eye.

J. Eugene Fox

Lawrence, Kansas

Contents

1 / Auxins

Auxins, produced in the growing tip of higher plants, enter into nearly every facet of plant growth and development, yet for years it has been recognized that the essential feature of auxin action is a stimulation of cell enlargement that is expressed in a variety of ways among the tissues and organs of a growing plant. How auxins in amounts as little as 10^{-8} molar cause cells to enlarge has been the subject of a vast amount of work with pitifully few lasting conclusions.

In the early 1960's, however, new lines of research of a type illustrated by the two papers presented here yielded promising results. It began to appear as though new protein and new RNA must be synthesized in order for cells to enlarge, a conclusion based in part on the elegant experiments of Joe Key at Purdue University, which constitute the first reading in this section. The reader may wish to take particular notice of the evidence that suggests that auxins play a part in cell enlargement through their regulation of nucleic acid synthesis by some as yet unknown mechanism.

Of course one would like to know more about auxin action at the polynucleotide level, and at least one promising lead was turned up very recently by a group working under the direction of Arthur Galston at Yale, whose paper is the second of the series. Evidence was presented that an auxin is actually bound into a low molecular weight RNA. The discussion of the possible significance of this incorporation makes fascinating reading.

Ribonucleic Acid and Protein Synthesis as Essential Processes for Cell Elongation

Joe L. Key

Reports of changes in RNA and protein metabolism associated with cell expansion are numerous. Results often depend on whether studies on cell expansion were done with intact plants or with excised parts. A net increase in protein content is usually associated with intact cell extension [6, 15, 17, 30], while excised tissues usually show a net decrease [9, 18, 30, 33]. A possible exception to the latter phenomenon was reported by Thimann and Loos [32] for excised potato and artichoke tissue. In these tissues, auxin stimulated the synthesis of protein over a 4-day period. Burroughs and Bonner [8] demonstrated protein synthesis associated with only slight variation in protein content during growth of excised coleoptile tissue. However, auxin did not affect the amount of C^{14}-amino acid incorporated into protein of the coleoptile tissue during 6 hours. Changes in specific activities and amounts of certain enzymes occur in association with cell elongation [3, 7, 14, 27, 28].

Studies on changes in RNA metabolism associated with cell expansion are equally complex. There is usually a progressive increase in RNA content per cell from the apical meristem through the zone of radial enlargement [15, 17], but in corn mesocotyl tissue [19], there was a net decrease in RNA per cell associated with cell expansion and maturation. The association of RNA with various cell organelles, as measured by differential centrifugation, changes in certain tissues during cell expansion and maturation [10, 19, 23, 29]. In excised tissues, a net decrease in RNA is usually associated with cell expansion [10, 20, 33, 35]. With corn mesocotyl, growth-promoting concentrations of auxin enhanced the rate of RNA breakdown [20, 33], but this was not observed in soybean hypocotyl tissue [18, 21]. In the expanding zone of excised soybean hypocotyl, auxin enhanced C^{14}-nucleotide incorporation into RNA [21], but this did not occur with corn mesocotyl [20]. The differences in RNA metabolism in elongating zones of soybean hypocotyl and corn mesocotyl may be attributable to differences in the degradative metabolism of RNA in these tissues. Corn mesocotyl has been shown to have more ribonuclease activity than soybean hypocotyl [34], and low concentrations of auxin enhance ribonuclease activity in corn mesocotyl during excised growth [30]. There is little or no change in ribonuclease activity of soybean hypocotyl during excised growth with or without auxin. The growth rate of corn root tips correlates positively with the RNA content of the tissue [35].

Reprinted by permission of the author and publisher from *Plant Physiology*, 39: 365–370, 1964. This work was supported by Public Health Service Research Grant GM 10157–03 from the National Institutes of Health.

Woodstock and Skoog [36] hypothesized that the amount of RNA synthesis by the cells of the root apex determines their subsequent rate of elongation. They also showed that IAA inhibited growth and RNA synthesis in the corn root.

Many lines of evidence support the view that RNA and protein synthesis may function during cell expansion, although no definitive experiments have been done. Developments in the field of protein and nucleic acid biochemistry provide a background of information on specific inhibitors which facilitate the study of RNA and protein syntheses. First, the antibiotic actinomycin D inhibits DNA-dependent synthesis of RNA by RNA polymerase at low concentrations [16] and leads to an inhibition of protein synthesis [13, 22]. DNA synthesis is inhibited only at higher concentrations [16]. Secondly, puromycin is an effective inhibitor of protein synthesis [1, 26]. Presumably by formation of abnormal messenger RNA, 8-azaguanine inhibits protein synthesis in bacteria while only slightly affecting RNA synthesis [9]. Also, the demonstration that part or all messenger or informational RNA is unstable (rapid turnover) in many systems [22, 25] would implicate continued RNA synthesis for the normal complete development of a cell.

Using the elongating zone of the soybean hypocotyl and actinomycin D, puromycin, and 8-azaguanine as specific inhibitors, the essentiality of RNA and protein synthesis for cell elongation was investigated. The data show that RNA and protein synthesis are essential for cell elongation in soybean hypocotyl tissue. There also is suggestive evidence that the role of auxin in regulating cell elongation may be associated with the control of RNA and/or protein synthesis.

Materials and Methods

Soybean seeds (*Glycine max*, var. Hawkeye) were germinated as previously described [21]. After 3 days a 1-cm section of hypocotyl was excised between 0.25 and 1.25 cm below the cotyledon and placed in a 1% sucrose solution at 2 to 4°. Samples (usually 0.8 or 1.0 g) of tissue were removed, blotted dry, weighed, and placed in the incubation medium. The basic medium consisted of a 1% sucrose solution containing 5×10^{-3} M KH_2PO_4 (neutralized to pH 6.0 with NH_4OH) and 20 μg/ml streptomycin. The potassium salt of 2,4-dichlorophenoxyacetic acid (2,4-D) was used at pH 6.0. Incubations were done at 30° in 5 ml of solution contained in 50-ml Erlenmeyer flasks with continuous shaking.

RNA analyses and C^{14}-nucleotide incorporation studies were conducted as previously described [21]. The following procedure was used in studies on C^{14}-amino acid incorporation into protein. Tissue which had been incubated in C^{14}-amino acid was homogenized in a Virtis 45 homogenizer at 2 to 4° in Tris buffer (0.01 M, pH 7.5) containing 0.2 mg/ml of C^{12}-

leucine. The homogenates were filtered through glass wool. An aliquot of the filtrate was removed and adjusted to 5% trichloroacetic acid. After shaking, the samples were centrifuged at $1000 \times g$ for 10 minutes ($0°$), decanted, and the pellet suspended in 5% trichloroacetic acid. Centrifugation was repeated and the pellets were dissolved in 1 N NaOH containing 0.2 mg/ml of C^{12}-leucine. After 10 minutes at $37°$, the samples were chilled to 2 to $4°$, and trichloroacetic acid was added to give a final acid concentration of 5%. Centrifugation was repeated followed by a 5% trichloroacetic acid wash. The pellet was dissolved in 2.0 N NH$_4$OH. Aliquots were plated, dried, and counted in a gas flow counter equipped with a micromil window. Samples with C^{14}-amino acid added at homogenization and prepared in this manner were free of radioactivity.

ATP-8-C^{14} (3.2 μc/mg) and L-leucine-U-C^{14} (840 μc/mg) were purchased from Schwarz Bio-Research.

Results

Actinomycin D, 8-azaguanine, and puromycin were tested for their capacity to alter the rate of growth of the elongating zones of excised soybean hypocotyl tissue. RNA and protein synthesis as altered by auxin or an inhibitor also were studied. Table 1 illustrates the inhibition by actinomycin of expansive growth and RNA synthesis in auxin-treated tissue. Auxin was used to provide conditions for optimum growth and

TABLE 1

Concentration Effects on Inhibition by Actinomycin D of
Growth and RNA Synthesis

Tissue (0.8 g) was incubated at $30°$ in a water bath shaker in a solution containing 1% sucrose, 5×10^{-3} M KH$_2$PO$_4$ (neutralized to pH 6.0 with NH$_4$OH), and 20 μg/ml streptomycin. 2,4-D was added as the potassium salt at pH 6.0. The 1-cm section of hypocotyl tissue used in all experiments was taken at 0.25 to 1.25 cm below the cotyledons and represents the zone of maximum cell expansion with no associated cell division. All treatments contained 10 μg/ml 2,4-D and 0.5 μc ATP-8-C^{14} (3.2 μc/mg). Data are from a single experiment, with each treatment being replicated 3 times.

Actinomycin D μg/ml	Increase ft wt % control	Mg RNA/g fr wt	Cpm/g fr wt in RNA
0.0	100	1.99	10,550
0.4	75	1.87	5,530
2.0	54	1.78	1,560
10.0	33	1.73	1,270
50.0	21	1.72	970

RNA synthesis. Synthesis of RNA was inhibited more than growth. This phenomenon will be discussed in relation to the data in table 4. Of interest here, is the large decrease in RNA content following actinomycin D treatment which parallels the inhibition of C^{14}-nucleotide incorporation into RNA. Time course studies show that actinomycin inhibited RNA synthesis in control and auxin-treated tissue to about the same extent, with the level of inhibition increasing with time (table 2). Actinomycin

TABLE 2

Time Study on the Inhibition of RNA Synthesis by Actinomycin D

Tissue was incubated as described in table 1.

Incu-bation Interval (hr)	No 2,4-D			10 μg/ml 2,4-D		
	Mg RNA/g fr wt	Cpm/g fr wt in RNA	Cpm/mg RNA	M gRNA/g fr wt	Cpm/g fr wt in RNA	Cpm/mg RNA
			No Actinomycin D			
0–2	1.78	1,860	1,040	1.80	2,020	1,125
0–4	1.76	4,835	2,740	1.84	6,045	3,280
0–8	1.71	12,575	7,350	1.84	14,740	8,020
			10 μg/ml Actinomycin D			
0–2	1.77	735	415	1.69	620	365
0–4	1.73	1,020	590	1.59	970	610
0–8	1.63	1,420	870	1.54	1,290	840

completely eliminated the auxin-induced component of C^{14}-nucleotide incorporation. The data in table 2 show that auxin caused a maintenance of RNA in this tissue relative to controls. In the absence of RNA synthesis, a greater loss of RNA occurred in auxin-treated tissue than in the controls (table 2).

The effects of 8-azaguanine on growth and RNA metabolism over an 8-hour period are presented in table 3. Growth of auxin-treated tissue was depressed by azaguanine similarly to the inhibition by actinomycin. As with actinomycin, the content of RNA decreased with increasing concentration of azaguanine, but the incorporation of C^{14}-nucleotide into RNA was only slightly affected. As in bacteria [9], the incorporation of C^{14}-nucleotide into RNA proceeded at or near the normal rate in soybean tissue in the presence of azaguanine even though there was a large decrease in RNA.

The effects of actinomycin D, 8-azaguanine, and puromycin on cell expansion are illustrated in tables 4, 5, and 6. Growth of control tissue was only slightly inhibited by actinomycin during the initial 2 hours of incubation, whereas inhibition was somewhat greater in auxin-treated tissue.

TABLE 3

Effect of 8-Azaguanine on Growth and ATP-8-C^{14} Incorporation into RNA

Experimental conditions same as described in table 1.

8-Azaguanine M	Increase fr wt % Control	Mg RNA/g fr wt	Cpm C^{14} in RNA	Cpm/mg RNA
0	100	1.99	10,550	5,300
0.5×10^{-3}	71	1.82	9,620	5,280
1.5×10^{-3}	54	1.77	9,320	5,260
2.5×10^{-3}	45	1.72	9,380	5,450
3.5×10^{-3}	42	1.71	9,660	5,650

TABLE 4

Time Study on Inhibition by Actinomycin D of Expansive Growth of Soybean Hypocotyl Tissue

Initial fresh weight of tissue was 800 mg. Incubation conditions same as in table 1. Data reported are means (with standard error) of 6 experiments; each treatment being replicated in each of the 6 experiments.

Growth interval (hr)	Control		10 μg/ml 2,4-D	
	Increase fr wt (mg)	% Inhibition	Increase fr wt (mg)	% Inhibition
	0 Actinomycin D			
0–2	95 ± 5	—	158 ± 9	—
2–4	95 ± 5	—	163 ± 8	—
4–8	123 ± 11	—	320 ± 7	—
	10 μg/ml Actinomycin D			
0–2	83 ± 4	11.9 ± 2.2	107 ± 5	30.7 ± 5.2
2–4	38 ± 5	59.5 ± 4.5	60 ± 4	63.3 ± 1.8
4–8	35 ± 4	74.9 ± 2.7	50 ± 8	84.3 ± 2.6

The inhibition of growth increased with time, but the inhibition of auxin-treated tissue relative to control tissue remained greater. Pretreatment of the tissue for 2 hours with auxin did not affect the subsequent inhibition of growth by actinomycin (table 5). Conversely, pretreatment of the tissue with actinomycin for 2 hours nearly erased the ability of the tissue to expand in response to auxin. Thus, it appears that the expansion of cells elongating at a constant maximum rate in response to auxin can be reduced in a relatively short time by actinomycin, whereas cells previously exposed to actinomycin have lost their sensitivity to auxin. The ratio of growth of auxin-treated to control tissue was 2.05 and 1.40 in the absence and presence of actinomycin, respectively.

TABLE 5

Influence of Treatment Time on the Inhibition of Auxin-
Induced Cell Expansion by Actinomycin D

Data averages of 3 experiments, with duplicate samples in each. Initial
fresh weight was 800 mg. Incubation conditions same as in table 1.
Actinomycin D was used at 10 μg/ml; 2,4-D at 10 μg/ml.

Growth Interval (hr)	Treatment*					
	A	B	C	D	E	F
	Increase fr wt (mg)					
0–2	95	83	158	107	158	83
2–4	95	38	163	60	100	50
4–8	123	35	320	50	70	38

* A, Zero 2,4-D; B, Zero 2,4-D + actinomycin D at zero time; C, 2,4-D
at zero time; D, 2,4-D and actinomycin D at zero time; E, 2,4-D at zero
time, actinomycin D at 2 hours; F, actinomycin D at time zero, 2,4-D at 2
hours.

Puromycin and 8-azaguanine inhibited cell expansion over an 8-hour
interval by 45 to 65% (table 6). As with actinomycin D, the inhibition
of growth increased with time and was greater in auxin-treated than in
control tissue, although the difference was not as great as with actinomycin.

TABLE 6

Inhibition by 8-Azaguanine and Puromycin of
Expansive Growth of Soybean Hypocotyl
Tissue

Incubation conditions were as described in table 1.
Data are average of 3 experiments.

Growth Interval (hr)	Treatment		
	None	Azaguanine (2.5 $\times$ 10^{-3} M)	Puromycin (5.0 $\times$ 10^{-4} M)
	Increase in fr wt (mg) Control		
0–2	95	88	80
2–4	95	57	40
4–8	123	40	15
Total	313	185	135
	10 μg/ml 2,4-D		
0–2	158	136	120
2–4	163	117	65
4–8	320	63	45
Total	641	316	230

Actinomycin D, 8-azaguanine, and puromycin are effective inhibitors of expansive growth (tables 4, 5, and 6) of soybean hypocotyl. The time course studies support the view that after about 2 hours these cells had exhausted a large portion of some component(s) essential to elongation. Although by somewhat different mechanisms, these compounds should lead to an inhibition of protein synthesis. Thus, preliminary experiments have been conducted to test the effects of these compounds on amino acid incorporation into protein of soybean hypocotyl tissue.

TABLE 7

Effects of 2,4-D and Actinomycin D on Leucine-C^{14} Incorporation into Soybean Hypocotyl Tissue

Incubation conditions same as in table 1 except that tissue was incubated for 2 hours. Actinomycin D used at 10 μg/ml.

Experiment No.*	Addition	No 2,4-D	10 μg/ml 2,4-D
		cpm/g fr wt**	
1	None	24,350	28,300
	Actinomycin	22,700	24,400
2	None	14,790	15,985
	Actinomycin	13,575	13,775
3	None	5,720	6,260
	Actinomycin	5,400	5,325

* Data for experiments 1, 2 and 3 represent averages of 2 separate experiments with duplicate samples in each. 0.5, 0.25, and 0.10 μc leucine-U-C^{14} used in a volume of 5 ml in experiments 1, 2, and 3 respectively.

** cpm/g fr wt in trichloroacetic acid-insoluble residue are corrected for any differences in total uptake of leucine-C^{14} by the tissue.

Data in tables 7 and 8 show that leucine-U-C^{14} was effectively incorporated into protein by soybean hypocotyl. Moreover, auxin caused an increase in leucine incorporation into the trichloroacetic acid-insoluble material by 5 to 16% in 8 separate experiments over a 2-hour interval (no stimulation by auxin was observed after the initial 2 hours of incubation). Actinomycin D, at a concentration which inhibited RNA synthesis by about 60% inhibited leucine incorporation by only 5 to 8% over a 2 hour interval (inhibition reached 10 to 12% after RNA synthesis was 90% inhibited). More important, actinomycin D nearly eliminated the auxin-induced component of leucine incorporation. At the concentrations used, azaguanine and puromycin were more effective than actinomycin D in inhibiting leucine incorporation, but the apparent stimulation by auxin of leucine incorporation persisted in the presence of both azaguanine and puromycin.

TABLE 8

Comparative Effects of Actinomycin D, 8-Azaguanine, and Puromycin
on Leucine-C^{14} Incorporation into Protein of Soybean Hypocotyl Tissue

Soybean hypocotyl tissue (0.8 g) was incubated as described in table 1 for 2 hours
in 0.25 μc uniformly labeled leucine-C^{14}. Data are from 2 closely duplicating experiments with each number representing an average of 6 observations.

Addition	2,4-D		2,4-D	
	0	10 μg/ml	0	10 μg/ml
	cpm/g fr wt* (in protein)		cpm/g fr wt** (Total uptake)	
None	11,660	14,040	30,000	33,450
10 μg/ml Actinomycin D	8,480	9,480	23,450	24,530
2.5 $\times$ 10^{-3} M 8-Azaguanine	6,340	7,770	19,220	22,200
5 $\times$ 10^{-4} M Puromycin	5,360	6,840	17,800	20,600

* Actual cpm incorporated into protein/g fresh weight.
** Total uptake of C^{14}-leucine by the tissue (cpm/g fresh weight).

Although no data are presented, about 10 to 12% of the total C^{14} incorporated into trichloroacetic acid-insoluble material was extractable in
lipid solvents. This fraction was not affected by auxin. After 6 N alkaline
hydrolysis (at 110° for 18 hours) of the residue after lipid extraction, the
detectable radioactivity chromatographed with standard C^{14}-leucine. Of
the C^{14}-nucleotide incorporated into RNA, about 70% was present in
AMP and 30% in GMP in alkaline hydrolysates of total RNA. No C^{14}-
nucleosides were detectable. Auxin did not affect the distribution of label
in the radioactive nucleotides.

Discussion

Actinomycin D, 8-azaguanine, and puromycin were used in an analysis
of RNA and protein synthesis associated with normal and auxin-induced
cell elongation in excised soybean hypocotyl tissue. The specific actions
of actinomycin, azaguanine, and puromycin are very different, yet they
have one property in common. They inhibit protein synthesis. In bacteria
the inhibition of protein synthesis is accomplished by (1) inhibition of
DNA-dependent RNA synthesis by actinomycin D [16] resulting in a rate
limiting supply of template RNA [22], (2) formation of defective or
nonsense RNA by incorporation of azaguanine into RNA [9] leading to
a shortage of messenger RNA, and (3) inhibition of one of the final steps
of protein synthesis in the case of puromycin [26]. The data presented
are consistent with the view, but do not prove, that the proposed actions
of actinomycin D, 8-azaguanine, and puromycin in bacteria are operative
in soybean hypocotyl tissue. Leucine-C^{14} incorporation into protein of

soybean hypocotyl was not inhibited as much by these chemicals (at comparable concentrations) as bacterial protein synthesis. This observation is strongly suggestive of considerable, relatively stable messenger or template RNA in this tissue, whereas messenger RNA (d RNA) of bacteria appears to be primarily of the unstable type [22, 25]. There is, however, evidence that stable messenger RNA is formed in developing bacterial spores [11]. It is tempting to speculate that only those proteins associated with changing metabolic function and activity of plant cells are made on relatively unstable RNA templates, and that the formation of these proteins would be subject to marked inhibition by the compounds used.

From our observations and the suggested action of the inhibitors, it appears that some protein and the associated template RNA essential to the process of cell expansion turn over more rapidly than the total protein and bulk template RNA. Presumably the protein is an enzyme(s) associated with some limiting system in the growth complex. Inhibition of the synthesis of either the template RNA or the associated protein results in a marked inhibition of cell elongation. This interpretation of the data implies that the process of cell elongation is actually under gene regulation with information release occurring through the DNA-directed formation of template RNA and finally synthesis of the regulating enzyme(s). The role of auxin in regulating cell elongation seems to be intimately associated with the regulation of the synthesis of RNA and/or protein. Enhanced nuclear activity must ultimately regulate the growth response to exogenous auxin. The following evidence supports these suggestions.

When sections of soybean hypocotyl were incubated in solutions containing 10 μg/ml actinomycin D, cell elongation proceeded at about 90% of the normal rate for 2 hours; inhibition was significantly greater in the case of auxin-treated tissue. Inhibition of growth was greater after 2 hours and reached 75 to 85% after 4 hours, remaining somewhat higher in auxin-treated tissue. A part of the delay in inhibition of growth by actinomycin D can be attributed to the time required for the chemical to penetrate and inhibit at the site of action (presumably the chromatin). However, synthesis of RNA was inhibited by 60% during the initial 2 hours and reached 90 to 95% within 4 hours. Although there is no direct evidence, it appears that a part of the delay in inhibition by actinomycin may be attributed to the time required to deplete the supply of unstable template RNA and the associated protein. Growth was effectively inhibited by 8-azaguanine and puromycin over the 8-hour period. However, a greater proportion of the auxin-induced component of growth was realized in the presence of 8-azaguanine and puromycin than with actinomycin D (ratios of auxin growth to control growth were 2.05, 1.4, 1.7, and 1.7 for untreated, actinomycin D-, 8-azaguanine-, and puromycin-treated tissue, respectively). After pretreatment of cells with actinomycin D, no appreciable growth response to auxin occurred, but cells induced by auxin remained sensitive to actinomycin D inhibition (table 5).

Auxin enhanced C^{14}-nucleotide incorporation into RNA. This effect was negated by actinomycin D. Similarly, results from preliminary experiments show an auxin enhancement of leucine-C^{14} incorporation into protein, and again actinomycin D essentially eliminated the response. In the presence of 8-azaguanine and puromycin, the stimulation by auxin of leucine-C^{14} incorporation into protein occurred, as with untreated tissue (no inhibitor). Thus, the auxin enhancement of growth, RNA synthesis, and apparently protein synthesis in soybean hypocotyl is sensitive to actinomycin D. But more of the auxin response occurs in the presence of 8-azaguanine and puromycin than in the presence of actinomycin D. From these observations, it would appear that the action of auxin in regulating the rate of cell elongation is more closely associated with the control of RNA synthesis than with protein synthesis. These data provide evidence in support of Skoog's suggestion that the action of auxin is intimately associated with the control of nucleic acid synthesis [31], by as yet some unknown mechanism.

Summary

RNA and protein synthesis associated with cell elongation of excised soybean hypocotyl tissue were investigated using actinomycin D, 8-azaguanine, and puromycin. The data presented are consistent with the view that the proposed actions of actinomycin D, 8-azaguanine, and puromycin in bacteria are operative in soybean hypocotyl tissue.

Based on the action of the inhibitors and the effects of these chemicals on cell elongation, it is concluded that RNA and protein synthesis are essential for the process of cell elongation to proceed at the normal rate. Moreover, the enhancement by 2,4-dichlorophenoxyacetic acid of the rate of cell elongation requires active RNA synthesis, and in turn protein synthesis. Presumably the rate of formation of some specific RNA is enhanced by auxin (either directly or indirectly) leading to an increased supply of some limiting enzyme or enzyme system. The way in which auxin alters RNA synthesis remains obscure.

Literature Cited

1. Arlinghaus, R., G. Fauelukes, and R. Schweet. 1963. A ribosome-bound intermediate in polypeptide synthesis. Biochem. Biophys. Res. Commun. 11: 92–96.

2. Basler, E. and K. Nakazawa. 1961. Some effects of 2,4-D on nucleic acids of cotton cotyledon tissue. Botan. Gaz. 122: 228–32.

3. Berger, J. and G. S. Avery, Jr. 1943. The mechanism of auxin action. Science 98: 454–55.

4. Biswas, B. B. and S. P. Sen. 1959. Relationships between auxins and nucleic acid synthesis in coleoptile tissue. Nature 183: 1824–25.

5. Bonner, J. and R. S. Bandurski. 1952. Studies on the physiology, pharmacology, and biochemistry of auxins. Ann. Rev. Plant Physiol. 3: 59–86.

6. Brown, R. and D. Broadbent. 1950. The development of cells in the growing zone of the root. J. Exptl. Botany 1: 249–63.

7. Brown, R. and E. Robinson. 1955. Cellular differentiation and the development of enzyme proteins in plants. In: Biological Specificity and Growth. E. G. Butler, ed. p 93–118. Princeton University Press, Princeton, New Jersey.

8. Burroughs, H. and J. Bonner. 1953. Effects of IAA on metabolic pathways. Arch. Biochem. Biophys. 46: 279–90.

9. Chantrenne, H. and S. Dueruex. 1960. Action de 8-azaguanine sur la synthesis des proteines et des acides nucleiques chez *Bacillus cereus*. Biochem. Biophys. Acta 39: 486–99.

10. Cherry, J. H. 1962. Ribonucleic acid metabolism during growth of excised root tips from normal and X-irradiated corn seeds. Biochem. Biophys. Acta 55: 487–94.

11. del Valle, M. R. and A. I. Aronson. 1962. Evidence for the synthesis of stable informational RNA required for bacterial spore formation. Biochem. Biophys. Res. Commun. 9: 421–25.

12. Galston, A. W. and W. K. Purves. 1960. The mechanism of action of auxin. Ann. Rev. Plant Physiol. 11: 239–76.

13. Haywood, A. M. and R. L. Sinsheimer. 1963. Inhibition of protein synthesis in *E. coli* protoplasts by actinomycin-D. J. Mol. Biol. 6: 247–49.

14. Heyes, J. K. 1959. The nucleic acids and plant growth and development. Symp. Soc. for Exptl. Biol. 13: 365–85.

15. Heyes, J. K. 1960. Nucleic acid changes during cell expansion in the root. Proc. Royal Soc. (London) 152: 218–30.

16. Hurwitz, J., J. J. Furth, M. Malamy, and M. Alexander. 1962. The inhibition of the enzymatic synthesis of RNA and DNA by actinomycin D and proflavin. Proc. Natl. Acad. Sci. 48: 1222–30.

17. Jensen, W. A. 1957. The incorporation of C^{14}-adenine and C^{14}-phenylalanine by developing root-tip cells. Proc. Natl. Acad. Sci. 43: 1038–46.

18. Key, J. L. and J. B. Hanson. 1961. Some effects of 2,4-D on soluble nucleotides and nucleic acid of soybean seedlings. Plant Physiol. 36: 145–52.

19. Key, J. L., J. B. Hanson, H. A. Lund, and A. E. Vatter. 1961. Changes in cytoplasmic particulates accompanying growth in the mesocotyl of *Zea mays*. Crop. Sci. 1: 5–8.

20. Key, J. L. 1963. Studies on 2,4-D-induced changes in ribonucleic acid metabolism in excised corn mesocotyl tissue. Weeds 11: 177–81.

21. Key, J. L. and J. C. Shannon. 1964. Enhancement by auxin of RNA synthesis in excised soybean hypocotyl tissue. Plant Physiol. 39: 360–64.

22. Levinthal, C., A. Keynan, and A. Higa. 1962. Messenger RNA turnover and protein synthesis in *B. subtilis* inhibited by actinomycin D. Proc. Natl. Acad. Sci. 48: 1631–38.

23. Lund, H. A., A. E. Vatter, and J. B. Hanson. 1958. Biochemical and cytological changes accompanying growth and differentiation in the roots of *Zea mays*. J. Biophys. Biochem. Cytol. 4: 87–98.

24. Masuda, Y. 1959. Role of cellular RNA in the growth response of Avena coleoptile to auxin. Physiol. Plantarum 12: 324–35.

25. Midgley, J. E. M. and B. J. McCarthy. 1962. The synthesis and kinetic behavior of DNA-like RNA in bacteria. Biochem. Biophys. Acta 61: 696–717.

26. Nathans, D., G. von Ehrenstein, R. Monro, and F. Lipmann. 1962. Protein synthesis from aminoacyl-soluble RNA. Federation Proc. 21: 127–33.

27. Robinson, E. and R. Brown. 1952. The development of the enzyme complement in growing root cells. J. Exptl. Botany 3: 356–74.

28. Robinson, E. and R. Brown. 1954. Enzyme changes in relation to cell growth in excised root tissues. J. Exptl. Botany 5: 71–78.

29. Setterfield, G. 1961. Structure and composition of plant-cell organelles in relation to growth and development. Can. J. Botany 39: 465–89.

30. Shannon, J. C. and J. B. Hanson. 1962. Ribonuclease activity as a function of growth in the corn mesocotyl. Plant Physiol. suppl. 37: xx.

31. Skoog, F. 1954. Substances involved in normal growth and differentiation of plants. Brookhaven Symp. in Biol. 6 (BNL 258): 1–21.

32. Thimann, K. V. and G. M. Loos. 1957. Protein synthesis during water uptake by tuber tissue. Plant Physiol. 32: 274–79.

33. West, S. H., J. B. Hanson, and J. L. Key. 1960. Effect of 2,4-D on the nucleic acid and protein content of seedling tissue. Weeds 8: 333–40.

34. Wilson, C. and J. C. Shannon. 1963. The distribution of ribonucleases in corn, cucumber, and soybean seedlings. Biochem. Biophys. Acta 68: 311–13.

35. Woodstock, L. W. and F. Skoog. 1960. Relationships between growth rates and nucleic acid contents of inbred lines of corn. Am. J. Botany 47: 713–16.

36. Woodstock, L. W. and F. Skoog. 1962. Distributions of growth, nucleic acids, and nucleic acid synthesis in seedling roots of *Zea mays*. Am. J. Botany 49: 623–33.

Recovery of Labeled Ribonucleic Acid Following Administration of Labeled Auxin to Green Pea Stem Sections

F. E. Bendaña
A. W. Galston
R. Kaur-Sawhney
P. J. Penny

Introduction

Recent experiments with vertebrates [14, 17, 21, 36], insects [6, 10] and plants [2, 18, 19, 26, 28, 34] have shown that RNA and protein synthesis are involved in the action of a wide variety of hormones. In particular, the blockage of hormone action by low concentrations of the RNA polymerase inhibitor, actinomycin D, indicates a connection between hormone action and the de novo synthesis of nucleic acids. It thus appears that the problem of explaining the molecular mechanisms involved in initial hormone action could be attacked by a study of the detailed mechanisms connecting hormones with nucleic acid metabolism.

Previous work from this laboratory [12, 16] has shown that a partial oxidation of the plant growth hormone indole-3-acetic acid (IAA) can complex in vitro with RNA extracted from growing pea stem segments. This finding led us to inquire whether similar complexes between auxin metabolites and nucleic acids could be formed in vivo.

Materials and Methods

Ten mm long subapical stem sections derived from 14- or 15-day-old light grown pea seedlings, var. Alaska [11] were incubated in petri dishes under fluorescent light (ca. 500 ft-c) in 10 ml of solution containing IAA, generally 10^{-4} M, 1% sucrose and 0.01 M K phosphate buffer, pH 6.0. This high concentration of IAA, which would be supraoptimal and inhibitory if fed to the conventionally employed etiolated sections, is on the ascending limb of the dose-response curve for green sections [13]. It is this fact, we believe, which renders our tracer experiments both technically feasible and physiologically meaningful. To work with stimulatory levels of IAA in etiolated tissues (i.e. ca. 10^{-6} M) would mean impossibly low levels of radioactivity in isolated fractions. To work with high levels (10^{-4} M) of IAA with etiolated tissue would mean injury and growth inhibition, rather than growth promotion.

Reprinted by permission of the authors and publisher from *Plant Physiology, 40:* 977–983, 1965. This work was supported by grants from the National Science Foundation, United States Public Health Service, and Herman Frasch Foundation.

After various time intervals ranging from 1 to 18 hours the sections were removed and washed, and their length and fresh weight measured. They were then stored in a deep freeze prior to extraction of RNA. To insure stability of RNA during the extraction procedure some investigators add ribonuclease inhibitors, such as bentonite [18, 19]. We found no need to do so since exogenous RNA supplied to our homogenate fractions in the presence of phenol could be quantitatively recovered. A further check involved a direct determination of ribonuclease activity in the pea stem and in fractions thereof. Although we can readily detect ribonuclease activity in one 5-mm stem section, no activity could be detected in any of the fractions in the flow sheet described, in which one hundred 10-mm sections were homogenized in the presence of phenol [20]. The frozen plant material (ca. 3 g) was homogenized to a still-frozen slurry with a prechilled mortar and pestle in 2 volumes of freshly redistilled phenol (90: 10 with Tris, v/v) and an equal volume of 0.01 M Tris-HCl buffer, pH 8.0. The homogenate was permitted to stand at room temperature for 1 hour, centrifuged at $4 \pm 1°$ for 20 minutes at $3500 \times g$, the phenol-water layer removed and extracted $4 \times$ at room temperature for 1 hour with 0.01 M Tris-HCl buffer, pH 8.0. The RNA in the combined aqueous layers was precipitated by the addition of 2% (final conc) potassium acetate and 2.5 to 3.0 volumes of cold ethanol (95%). This mixture was allowed to stand at $4 \pm 1°$ overnight, and the white flocculent precipitate harvested by centrifuging the mixture at $20,000 \times g$ for 20 minutes in the cold. The precipitate was dissolved in 2 ml of Tris-HCl buffer, pH 8.0, and centrifuged at $30,000 \times g$ for 20 minutes to remove any debris. The supernatant fraction was again treated with 2% potassium acetate and 2.5 to 3.0 volumes of cold ethanol and allowed to stand 30 minutes in an ice bath, after which the precipitate was again harvested by centrifugation and redissolved in 1 ml of Tris. This procedure was repeated 3 more times to yield a purified RNA (Ppt IV), which had a constant spectrum and specific activity. Reextraction of this fraction with phenol changed neither its spectrum nor its radioactivity. All work reported here was performed on Ppt IV, whose isolation is summarized in Fig. 1.

Ribonucleic acid was hydrolyzed with 0.3 M KOH at 37° according to the technique of Davidson and Smellie [7] and the monoribonucleotides separated electrophoretically by a slight modification of the Markham and Smith technique [23]. The buffer used was 0.05 M ammonium formate-formic acid, pH 3.4, containing 5% sucrose to decrease trailing of spots. The electrophoretic separation was performed with a Spinco Duostat and Durrum-type cell, with a voltage gradient of 9.8 v/cm, applied for 4 hours. The nucleotides were detected and marked under a UV lamp; the spots were then eluted with 0.01 N HCl, spectrally characterized and counted. Thin-layer chromatography was also used to separate the nucle-

EXTRACTION OF RNA FROM PEA STEM TISSUE

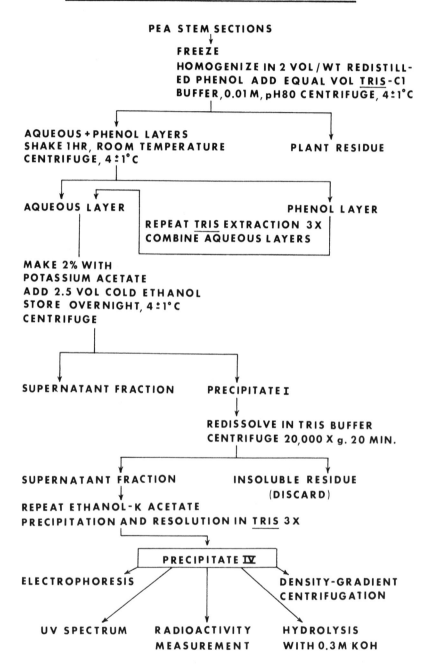

Fig. 1. Scheme for the isolation of pea RNA.

otides. The adsorbent was MN cellulose powder (300 G/DEAE cellulose) sold by Brinkmann, Inc. The developer was .01 N HCl, as recommended by Randerath [27]. The C¹⁴-IAA used in most of the experiments was a carboxyl-labeled product (16.9 mc/mM) synthesized by our colleague B. B. Stowe [31]. Both gas flow and scintillation counters were used for measurement of the radioactivity of the various fractions.

Results

Incorporation of Label into RNA

The fraction designated as precipitate IV was found to have the spectral characteristics of RNA (Fig. 2) and to be completely hydrolyzable by

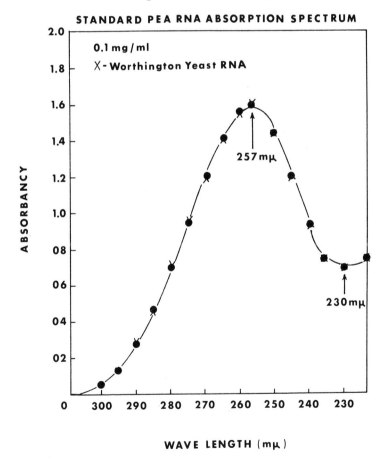

Fig. 2. Comparison of the spectral characteristics of pea and yeast RNA. RNA was dissolved in 0.01 M Tris-HCl buffer, pH 8.0, and characterized in a model 350 Perkin Elmer recording spectrophotometer.

crystalline ribonuclease. When extracted from stem tissues incubated with C^{14}-IAA, precipitate IV was also radioactive. The specific activity of this fraction was found to be unaltered by dialysis in the presence of cold IAA and by extraction with such organic solvents as ethanol, ethyl ether, chloroform and to further phenol extractions. No DNA could be detected in precipitate IV by the p-nitrophenylhydrazine method of Webb and Levy [35], no protein was detected by the Folin reagent [22] nor was any loss in material or specific activity found after treatment with 2-methoxyethanol, a material used by Kirby [20] to remove polysaccharides. It was thus concluded that the radioactivity found was an integral part of extracted RNA. The kinetics of incorporation of label from carboxyl C^{14}-IAA into precipitate IV are shown in Fig. 3.

The uptake of label from C^{14}-IAA into plant tissue rises as the concentration of IAA is increased (table 1) and with increasing length of the incubation period (table 2). The data of table 2 show also that under 5%

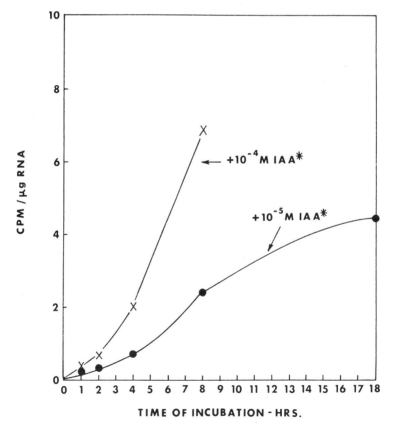

Fig. 3. Kinetics of incorporation of radioactivity from IAA into RNA as a function of IAA concentration.

TABLE 1

Relation Between Concentration of Applied Carboxyl-Labeled IAA (13.5 mc/mM) and Labeling of Extracted RNA (Precipitate IV).

Incubation time = 4 hours.

IAA (M)	% Increase in fr wt	Cpm per μg RNA
Control	15.4	0
10^{-6}	30.8	0.48
10^{-5}	46.2	1.19
10^{-4}	61.6	6.18
10^{-3}	73.0	27.6

TABLE 2

Kinetics of Uptake of Label from IAA into Sections and Incorporation into RNA

Initial IAA was 6×10^{-5} M; specific activity 16.9 mc/mM. 100 sections per treatment.

			Incubation Medium			
Time of treatment (hr)	Cpm per 4 μl	Total corrected cpm $\times 10^6$	% of counts remaining	Cpm as IAA in 4 μl*	Total corrected cpm as IAA $\times 10^6$	% of original IAA remaining
0	10,040	25.1	100	—	25.1	100
¼	8617	21.54	85.81	8880	22.20	88.44
½	8633	21.58	85.97	8544	21.36	85.09
1	8412	21.03	83.78	8202	20.50	81.67
2	8263	20.65	82.27	6873	17.17	68.40
4	7545	18.86	75.13	5115	12.78	50.91

	Sections			RNA (Precipitate IV)		
Time of treatment (hr)	Cpm in 2 sections	Total cpm in all sections	% of counts absorbed	mg RNA	cpm/μg RNA	Cpm in RNA/cpm absorbed $\times 100$
0	—	—	—	3.02	—	—
¼	1734.9	86,745	0.345	3.21	—	—
½	3526.3	176,315	0.702	3.74	0.3	0.636
1	9076.1	453,805	1.807	3.59	0.7	0.553
2	11,770	588,100	2.344	3.50	1.36	0.808
4	23,188.3	1,159,415	4.619	3.48	3.10	0.930

* 4 μl spotted on TLC and only cpm in R_F of IAA used.

of the total counts supplied were absorbed into the tissue during a 4-hour period, and that, at any time chosen, under 1% of the absorbed counts are found in RNA. The remainder of the counts must be located in other metabolites of IAA, not further investigated here. Such metabolites must include CO_2 or other volatile products which are not accounted for in sections or solution.

To investigate the specificity of IAA and of the carboxyl group as donors of label to RNA, methylene-labeled IAA and carboxyl- and methylene-labeled 2,4-dichlorophenoxyacetic acid (2,4-D), were fed to tissue and the resulting RNA isolated and counted. Table 3 shows that

TABLE 3

Comparative Effectiveness of Differentially Labeled Auxins as Donors of Label to RNA

Sections were incubated for 18 hours before RNA was extracted. Growth, as measured by the increase in fresh weight, was approximately equal in all 4 groups. All auxins supplied at 10^{-4} M.

Source of Label	Specific Activity $\mu c/mg$	Cpm Added $\times 10^6$	Total Cpm in RNA Fraction	Total RNA (mg)	$Cpm/\mu g$ RNA	Correction Factor IAA- $1C^{14} = 1$	Corrected $Cpm/\mu g$ RNA	Relative $Cpm/\mu g$
IAA-1C^{14}	96.6	36.9	150,520	3.150	47.78	1	47.78	100.00
IAA-2C^{14}	16.2	6.2	10,640	2.900	3.66	5.95	21.82	45.66
2,4-D-1C^{14}	8.9	4.3	2,240	3.335	0.67	8.58	5.77	12.07
2,4-D-2C^{14}	19.2	9.4	640	2.875	0.22	3.29	0.73	1.52

IAA is approximately 10 times more effective as a label donor than is 2,4-D, and that in each compound, carboxyl is 2 to 3 times more effective than methylene. This naturally raised the question of possible dismutation of the labeled compounds to smaller fragments, which could then be recycled, either photosynthetically or heterotrophically, to yield components of RNA. For comparison, therefore, labeled CO_2 was fed, in the presence of unlabeled 10^{-4} M IAA, to insure equality of the growth response. Like C^{14}-IAA, $C^{14}O_2$ is incorporated into RNA, but the pattern of labeling from the 2 sources is quite different. RNA obtained from sections fed IAA show a great preponderance of label in the adenylate and cytidylate regions, while RNA from sections fed CO_2 show a much more symmetrical distribution of label in the 4 nucleotides. The incorporation of label from both IAA and CO_2 was markedly inhibited by 10 $\mu g/ml$ actinomycin D (table 4), while the incorporation of label from $C^{14}O_2$ was unaffected by the presence of IAA and therefore of growth. It should be noted that auxin-induced growth is totally inhibited by the 10 $\mu g/ml$ actinomycin D (AMD) treatment. That some incorporation of $C^{14}O_2$ into RNA should be observed even in the presence of AMD is not unusual, since it is well known [24, 32] that polyphosphorylase, the enzyme respon-

TABLE 4

Effect of Actinomycin D (AMD) on Growth of Green Pea Stem Sections
and Labeling of RNA

The sections were grown for 18 hours. IAA concentration 10^{-4}M; AMD concentration
$10\mu g/ml$.*

| Treatment | | | % Increase in fr wt | Cpm/μg RNA | Inhibition (cpm/μg RNA) due to AMD |
IAA	CO$_2$	AMD			
—	—	—	35.4	—	
Labeled	Unlabeled	—	122.0	30.6	
Labeled	Unlabeled	+	38.4	24.6	6.00
—	Labeled	—	21.3	12.5	
—	Labeled	+	11.3	6.7	5.8
Unlabeled	Labeled	—	113.0	11.3	
Unlabeled	Labeled	+	33.6	5.5	5.8

* This concentration of AMD inhibits all auxin-induced growth measured as percentage increase in fresh weight.

sible for the addition of the terminal trinucleotide to s-RNA, is not inhibited by AMD. Although this reasoning may also be used to explain some of counts found in the C^{14}-IAA fed sections, approximately 18 cpm/μg RNA cannot be explained in this way (table 4). These data are interpreted as meaning that some of the counts going from fed IAA to extracted RNA arise from recycling of CO_2 or some other fragment of IAA, but that the remainder of the incorporation occurs by way of a more direct pathway, such as direct coupling of IAA to preexisting RNA.

Isolation of IAA from the Labeled RNA

To investigate the possibility that IAA might also bind per se to RNA in a form recoverable from the complex, a sample of labeled Ppt IV was hydrolyzed with KOH, as described above, and also by the Na_2CO_3 method devised by Zamecnik et al. [37]. After hydrolysis with KOH, the material was acidified to pH 2.8 to 3.0 with 0.01 N HCl and rapidly extracted 3 × with peroxide-free ethyl ether. While pure IAA partitioned 2.5% into the aqueous layer and 97.5% into the organic layer, the radioactivity of the complex partitioned 65% into the aqueous layer and 35% into the ethereal layer. This indicates that the label now exists in several different molecular species. The ethereal layer was taken down to dryness in a rotary flash evaporator at room temperature. The residue was taken up in 0.5 ml of absolute ethanol and separated by thin layer chromatography on silica gel, the solvent system being methyl acetate-isopropanol-25% ammonium hydroxide (45:35:20, v/v/v). The gel from indicated areas of the plates was scraped off and subjected to liquid scintillation counting according to the technique of Snyder and Stephens [30]. Under these conditions, where the R_F of IAA is 0.47 to 0.50, the major peak of radioactivity of the recovered silica gel occurred at the same position (Fig. 4). In another experiment, spraying the thin layer plate with the Prochazka reagent [27] produced a spot at the locus of IAA which was readily detected under an ultraviolet light and had an appearance identical with similarly treated authentic IAA. A positive Prochazka reaction at the locus of IAA was also found in unextracted alkaline hydrolyzates of the RNA and in ether extracts thereof. Control RNA, or RNA from $C^{14}O_2$ fed sections yielded no such spot or counts in their hydrolyzates when chromatogrammed. These results indicate that IAA or some metabolite of IAA complexes with a RNA fraction during growth of pea stem tissue.

Physical Characterization of the Labeled RNA

Labeled RNA derived from sections fed carboxyl-labeled IAA was separated in a sucrose density gradient (0–25%) according to the method of Brakke [4], using a Spinco model L ultracentrifuge and an SW25.1 rotor, at 24,000 rpm for 8 hours, in 0.01 M Tris-HCl buffer, pH 8.0 and 0.001 M $MgCl_2$. From the very first detection of labeled RNA, the 4S fraction was most heavily labeled, and even after 18 hours of incubation in labeled IAA, the 16S and 28S ribosomal peaks were unlabeled (Fig. 5). There is also a peak of labeling, but not of absorbancy, in the region between 4S and 16S, usually designated as messenger RNA. This peak would appear to have very high specific activity.

The question arises, is IAA initially incorporated into a 4S RNA fraction, or is it first incorporated into a heavier fraction, which is then broken down to 4S size? This was investigated by comparing the centrifugal distribution of radioactivity in labeled RNA produced from simultaneously applied C^{14}-IAA (13.5 mc/mM; 7.5 μc added) and H^3-uridine (4.6 c/mM; 100 μc added). RNA was obtained and separated centrifugally as previously described. A 2-channel scintillation spectrometer (ANS, Inc., Wallingford, Connecticut) permitted simultaneous determination of H^3 and C^{14} in each centrifugal fraction (Fig. 6). The counting efficiencies were as follows: in the H^3 channel, 15.7% with a 2.64% carryover from C^{14}; in the C^{14} channel 61.34% with a carryover of less than 0.09% from H^3. All plotted values were corrected for background, carryover and quenching.

It is obvious that tritiated uridine finds its way into all RNA fractions after a 6-hour incubation period. However, C^{14} from IAA, as previously found, is associated mainly with the 4S peak, secondarily with a peak in the usual vicinity of messenger RNA, and practically not at all with the 28S ribosomal peak. In the 28S peak, the molar ratio of uridine to IAA incorporation was approximately 8.0. However, in the 4S and 16S regions

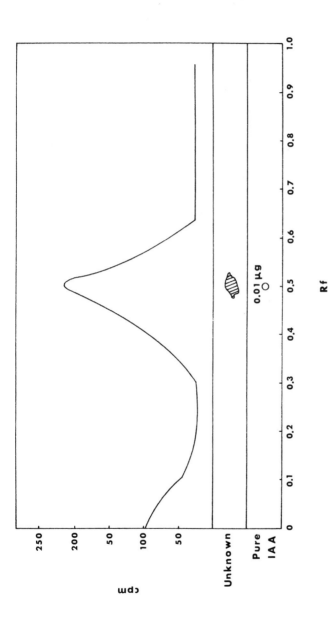

Fig. 4. Recovery of IAA from hydrolyzed RNA as shown by thin-layer chromatography on silica gel. Graphic representation of the average of 5 experiments. The pattern was obtained by removing the gel and determining the radioactivity at each R_F by liquid scintillation counting. IAA: specific activity 13.5 mc/mM; 170 cpm/mµg IAA; average cpm at R_F 0.5 was 250 cpm, or about 1.46 mµg IAA (8.3×10^{-10} moles). RNA content per spot applied = 30 µg (average M.W. 4s RNA = 30,000, about 80 nucleotide residues) or about 10^{-9} M. RNA: IAA counts ratio = $(10^{-9})/(8.3 \times 10^{-10})$ = 1.20. Therefore we have found approximately 1.0 mole of IAA per mole 4s RNA or one IAA per 80 nucleotide residues.

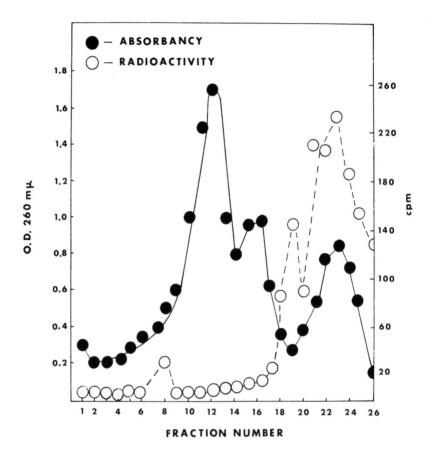

Fig. 5. Centrifugal profile of pea RNA in a 0 to 25% sucrose density gradient. One ml fractions were collected and a complete absorption spectrum obtained for each. From right to left, the 3 absorbancy peaks represent 4S, 16S and 28S fractions. These figures were obtained by comparison with known rat liver RNA.

the corresponding figure was less than 0.6. This substantiates the view that IAA is preferentially incorporated into light RNA fractions, and speaks against the large-scale unspecific incorporation of degradation products of IAA into general RNA synthesis.

Discussion

There are now several reports in the literature describing the binding of steroid hormones [25, 29, 33] and carcinogenic hydrocarbons [3, 8] to nucleic acids. In addition, there are reports that synthetic plant growth substances such as maleic hydrazide [5] and kinins [9] may be incorpo-

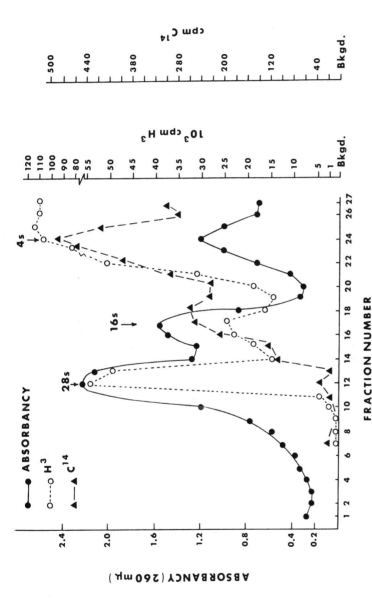

Fig. 6. Centrifugal profile and labeling pattern of pea stem RNA, obtained from sections simultaneously incubated for 6 hours with 100 μc H^3-uridine (specific activity 4.63 c/mM) and 1-C^{14}-IAA, (specific activity 13.5 mc/mM). Sucrose gradient 0 to 25% in Tris-HCl, (0.01 M pH 8.0, 10^{-3} M $MgCl_2$, ●——●, absorbency units; O----O, corrected cpm of tritium; ▲---▲, corrected cpm of carbon-14. Uridine is incorporated into all types of RNA while C^{14} from IAA is associated mainly with the lighter fractions even after this long incubation period.

rated into nucleic acids, where they substitute respectively, for normal pyrimidines and purines. The present report of the binding of IAA with RNA, while it is the first indication of complex formation between a native plant growth hormone and nucleic acid, falls into an established framework. It is also instructive to note that mitomycin and porfiromycin are believed to bind to nucleic acid only after reduction to an aromatic indole [15].

It is clear that carboxyl-labeled IAA donates label to the isolated precipitate IV in 2 ways: A) direct binding of intact IAA with RNA, from which form it is recoverable as such; and B) dismutation, probably into CO_2, followed by reutilization of the split products in de novo purine and pyrimidine biosynthesis. Neither the nature of the linkage between RNA and IAA nor the reason for the relatively heavy labeling of cytidylate and adenylate regions are clear. In view of the known turnover of cytidylate and adenylate at the amino acid acceptor end of transfer RNA [1] it is tempting to postulate an attachment of IAA at this point. We hope to obtain further information relative to this possibility.

If a complex between IAA and RNA does occur in vivo, what may be its significance and role in growth promotion? There are 3 obvious possibilities: A) The hormone, through complex formation with RNA, could be involved in removing it from the surface of another molecule, such as template DNA or ribosomal RNA. We have as yet no evidence relevant to this possibility. B) The formation of the hormone-RNA complex could confer upon the RNA greater stability toward degradative agents, such as ribonuclease. In support of this possibility, we have in fact already observed progressively slower ribonuclease action on RNA isolated from stem sections incubated for increasing periods with 10^{-4} M IAA. These results will be reported later in detail. C) The possibility also exists that the IAA molecule, or portion thereof, may possess informational value when attached to a particular locus in an RNA chain. The general conformational similarity between the indole nucleus and the purine nucleus makes this conjecture at least a possibility worth entertaining.

Summary

C^{14} from carboxyl-labeled indole-3-acetic acid (IAA) fed to excised, growing green pea stem sections is progressively incorporated into RNA extractable by phenol. The kinetics of incorporation resemble the kinetics of growth induction by IAA. C^{14} from methylene-labeled IAA and from carboxyl and methylene-labeled 2,4-dichlorophenoxyacetic acid were also incorporated into RNA, but with lower efficiency than from carboxyl-labeled IAA. Both growth and C^{14} incorporation into RNA were inhibited by 10 μg/ml actinomycin D. The label was incorporated into a light (4S) RNA fraction as shown by sucrose density gradient centrifugation, while tritiated uridine simultaneously applied was incorporated into ribosomal peaks as well. Alkaline hydrolysis, followed by separation of the nucleotides by paper electrophoresis and thin layer chromatography showed that the bulk of the C^{14} label is associated with adenylate and cytidylate regions. Some activity from fed labeled IAA was also detected in the form of unchanged IAA recovered from the alkaline hydrolyzate. It is concluded that some IAA couples per se with soluble RNA while some of it is degraded, and the split products including CO_2 are used in resynthesis of RNA components.

Literature Cited

1. Berg, P. 1961. Specificity in protein synthesis. Ann. Rev. Biochem. 30: 293–324.

2. Biswas, B. B. and S. P. Sen. 1959. Relationship between auxins and nucleic acid synthesis in coleoptile tissues. Nature 183: 1824–25.

3. Boyland, E. and B. Green. 1963. The effect of polycyclic hydrocarbons on the thermal denaturation of deoxyribonucleic acid. Biochem. J. 87: 14P–15P.

4. Brakke, M. K. 1953. Zonal separations by density-gradient centrifugation. Arch. Biochem. Biophys. 45: 275–90.

5. Callaghan, J. J., M. D. Appleton, W. Haab, and C. P. Portanova. 1962. Incorporation of C^{14}-labeled maleic hydrazide by RNA derived from *Saccharomyces cerevisiae*. Proc. Penn. Acad. Sci. 36: 91–95.

6. Clever, U. 1964. Actinomycin and puromycin: Effects on sequential gene activation by ecdysone. Science 146: 794–95.

7. Davidson, J. N. and R. M. S. Smellie. 1952. Phosphorous compounds in the cell. 2. The separation by ionophoresis on paper of the constituent nucleotides of ribonucleic acid. Biochem. J. 52: 594–99.

8. DeMaeyer, E. and J. De Maeyer-Guignard. 1964. Effects of polycyclic aromatic carcinogens on viral replication: Similarity to actinomycin D. Science 146: 650–51.

9. Fox, J. 1964. Incorporation of kinins into the RNA of plant tissue cultures. Plant Physiol. 39: xxxi.

10. Gall, J. G. and H. G. Callan. 1962. H^3 Uridine incorporation in lampbrush chromosomes. Proc. Natl. Acad. Sci. 48: 562–70.

11. Galston, A. W. and R. S. Baker. 1951. Studies on the physiology of light action. IV. Light enhancement of auxin-induced growth in green peas. Plant Physiol. 26: 311–17.

12. Galston, A. W., P. Jackson, R. Kaur-Sawhney, N. P. Kefford, and W. J. Meudt. 1964. Interactions of auxins with macromolecular constituents of pea seedlings. In: Régulateurs Naturels de la Croissance Végétale. Editions du Centre Natl. Res. Sci., Paris. p 251–64.

13. Galston, A. W. and R. Kaur. 1961. Comparative studies on the growth and light sensitivity of green and etiolated pea stem sections. In: Light and Life. W. D. McElroy and B. Glass, eds. Johns Hopkins press. p 687–705.

14. Hancock, R. L., R. F. Zelis, M. Shaw, and H. G. Williams-Ashman. 1962. Incorporation of ribonucleoside triphosphates into ribonucleic acid by nuclei of the prostate gland. Biochim. Biophys. Acta 55: 257–60.

15. Iyer, V. N. and W. Szybalski. 1964. Mitomycin and porfiromycin: Chemical mechanism of activation and cross-linking of DNA. Science 145: 55–58.

16. Kefford, N. P., R. Kaur-Sawhney, and A. W. Galston. 1963. Formation of a complex between a derivative of the plant hormone indoleacetic acid and ribonucleic acid from pea seedlings. Acta Chem. Scand. 17 Suppl. 1: 313–18.

17. Kenney, F. T. and F. J. Kull. 1963. Hydrocortisone-stimulated synthesis of nuclear RNA in enzyme induction. Proc. Natl. Acad. Sci. 50: 493–99.

18. Key, J. L. 1964. RNA and protein synthesis as essential processes for cell elongation. Plant Physiol. 39: 365–70.

19. Key, J. L. and J. C. Shannon. 1964. Enhancement by auxin of ribonucleic acid synthesis in excised hypocotyl tissue. Plant Physiol. 39: 360–64.

20. Kirby, K. S. 1956. A new method for the isolation of ribonucleic acids from mammalian tissue. Biochem. J. 64: 405–08.

21. Liao, S. and H. G. Williams-Ashman. 1962. An effect of testosterone on amino acid incorporation by prostatic ribonucleoprotein particles. Proc. Natl. Acad. Sci. U.S. 48: 1956–64.

22. Lowry, O. H., N. J. Rosenbrough, A. L. Farr, and R. J. Randall. 1951. Protein measurement with the Folin phenol reagent. J. Biol. Chem. 193: 265–73.

23. Markham, R. and J. D. Smith. 1962. The structure of ribonucleic acids. 2. The smaller products of ribonuclease digestion. Biochem. J. 52: 558–65.

24. Merits, I. 1963. Actinomycin inhibition of RNA synthesis in rat liver. Biochem. Biophys. Res. Commun. 10: 254–59.

25. Munck, A., J. F. Scott, and L. L. Engel. 1957. The interaction of steroid hormones and coenzyme components. Biochim. Biophys. Acta 36: 397–407.

26. Noodén, L. D. and K. V. Thimann. 1963. Evidence for a requirement for protein synthesis for auxin-induced cell enlargement. Proc. Natl. Acad. Sci. U.S. 50: 194–200.

27. Randerath, K. 1963. Thin-layer Chromatography. Academic Press, New York.

28. Roychoudhury, R. and S. P. Sen. 1964. Studies on the mechanism of auxin action: auxin regulation of nucleic acid metabolism in pea internodes and coconut milk nuclei. Physiol. Plantarum 17: 352–62.

29. Scott, J. F. and L. L. Engel. 1957. Molecular interaction between purines and steroids. Biochim. Biophys. Acta 23: 665–67.

30. Snyder, F. and N. Stephens. 1962. Quantitative carbon-14 and tritium assay of thin-layer chromatography plates. Anal. Biochem. 4: 128–31.

31. Stowe, B. B. 1963. Synthesis of high specific activity C^{14} carboxyl indoleacetic acid and of C^{14}-nitrile indoleacetonitrile. Anal. Biochem. 5: 107–15.

32. Tamaoki, T. and G. C. Mueller. 1962. Synthesis of nuclear and cytoplasmic RNA of Hela cells. Biochem. Biophys. Res. Commun. 9: 451–54.

33. Tso, P. O. and Ponzy Lu. 1964. Interaction of nucleic acids. I. Physical binding of thymine, adenine, steroids and aromatic hydrocarbons to nucleic acids. Proc. Natl. Acad. Sci. U.S. 51: 17–24.

34. Varner, J. E. 1964. Gibberellic acid controlled synthesis of α-amylase in barley endosperm. Plant Physiol. 39: 413–15.

35. Webb, J. M. and H. B. Levy. 1955. A sensitive method for the determination of deoxyribonucleic acid in tissues and microorganisms. J. Biol. Chem. 213: 107–17.

36. Wicks, W. D. and F. T. Kenney. 1964. RNA synthesis in rat seminal vesicles: stimulation by testosterone. Science 144: 1346–47.

37. Zamecnik, P. C., M. L. Stephenson, and J. F. Scott. 1960. Partial purification of soluble RNA. Proc. Natl. Acad. Sci. U.S. 46: 811–22.

2 / Gibberellins

Discovered much more recently than the auxins, gibberellins too are naturally occurring substances that profoundly affect plant growth at fantastically low concentrations. Gibberellin studies have gone through a cycle similar in many ways to that of the auxins, except much more condensed in time. After an initial cataloging in the 1950's of physiological responses to this class of growth hormone, attention has been focused more recently on their mode of action.

The two papers in this section attest to the fact that "gibberellinologists" are having an exciting time of it. Very recently Nitsan and Lang concluded that DNA synthesis is necessary for the elongation of at least some kinds of plant cells and that gibberellins enhance DNA and RNA synthesis to a considerable degree. The work on which these conclusions are based is represented by the first reading in this section. It will be evident that this paper makes a very nice companion piece for the report by Key in the first section.

The second reading in this section is by Varner and Chandra, who have also concluded that gibberellins act at the polynucleotide level. Their work, however, is based on a quite different biological effect of the growth substance. In a series of beautifully done experiments, it was shown that the well known increase in enzyme activity of seeds treated with gibberellins was due to *de novo* synthesis of the enzyme being studied. Particularly provocative are the last two sentences in the paper. Not only is an hypothesis offered relating gibberellin activity to gene translation but also methods to check this hypothesis experimentally are discussed.

DNA Synthesis in the Elongating Nondividing Cells of the Lentil Epicotyl and Its Promotion by Gibberellin

Joseph Nitsan
Anton Lang

Growth of plants proceeds by cell division and cell extension; the latter often proceeds mainly in 1 direction and is then called cell elongation. Since cell division is dependent on nuclear division it was obvious that it would be dependent on DNA synthesis. It was however found [12] that cell elongation may be inhibited by treating the tissue with FUDR* and other inhibitors of DNA synthesis. The inhibition by FUDR could be completely reversed with thymidine, but not with uridine. The tissues used were the lettuce hypocotyl and the lentil epicotyl, 2 tissues in which cell elongation is promoted by GA. The effect of the DNA inhibitors was evident both in the presence and absence of exogenous GA.

If cell elongation in these tissues, both that taking place without supply of exogenous GA and that induced by added GA, depends on DNA synthesis it should be possible to detect synthesis of this compound in the elongating cells. Furthermore, GA may be expected to promote this synthesis; FUDR may be expected to inhibit both the DNA synthesis observed in the absence of GA and the increased DNA synthesis in the presence of GA; and thymidine should reverse this inhibition.

Since presence of dividing cells in the investigated tissue would complicate any conclusions that may be derived from chemical determinations of DNA, or of DNA synthesis, it was particularly important to use a tissue which consists only of elongating, nondividing cells to investigate these problems.

In the present work we used the lentil epicotyl, as it had been found that this organ has a fairly constant number of cells while it elongates, regardless of presence or absence of GA, FUDR, and thymidine, alone or in combination [12].

Materials and Methods

Plant Material

Lentil seedlings [*Lens culinaris* Medik (*L. esculenta* Moench) cv. Persian; Washington State University, Pullman, Washington] were grown

* Abbreviations: GA, gibberellin; FUDR, 5-fluorode-oxyuridine; MAK, methylated-albumin-kieselguhr.

Reprinted by permission of A. Lang (J. Nitsan deceased) and publisher from *Plant Physiology*, 41: 965–970, 1966. This work was supported by the United States Atomic Energy Commission, Contract No. AT (11–1) 1338.

and handled as previously described [12]. The seeds were germinated in the dark at about 22°. After 48 hours, the seed coats were removed, the radicles cut back, and the seedlings incubated under shaking in basal medium (0.1 Hoagland's nutrient solution, containing 1000 units of penicillin GK per ml) plus test chemicals for periods of 48 hours or less, in the dark. Seedlings 48 hours after germination are referred to as seedlings in the initial state.

All determinations were made on the epicotyl, i.e. the internode above the cotyledons. The stem was cut at the points of attachment of the cotyledons and the first scale leaf; cotyledons, hypocotyl, root and the shoot apex were discarded. In previous experiments [12] it had been shown that the epicotyl grows, responds to GA and is inhibited by FUDR, at least during the period used in these experiments, both in the presence and the absence of the shoot tip.

Cell Counts

The number of cells per epicotyl was estimated using the haemocytometer method of Brown and Rickless [3]. A sample of 10 epicotyls was suspended in 25 ml of chromic acid and the cells in 4 aliquots of 2 μl each were counted.

Extraction and Estimation of DNA and RNA

The extraction procedure was essentially that of Smillie and Krotkov [15], with slight modifications. All operations up to the ethanol:ether extraction were carried out at 4°. Epicotyls were homogenized with 0.15 M NaCl–0.1 M EDTA buffer pH 8.0 by mortar and pestle. An equal volume of 40% (w/v) trichloroacetic acid was added immediately to the homogenate. After standing for 1 hour, the precipitate was collected by centrifugation and extracted successively with methanol (twice), ethanol, boiling ethanol:ether (1:1), and ether. The air-dried insoluble residue was extracted by alkaline hydrolysis; after this it was cooled to 0°, acidified with perchloric acid, and centrifuged. The precipitate was washed with cold 1% perchloric acid (twice) and the combined supernatant fraction was used for the estimation of RNA as phosphorus by King's method [10]. The insoluble residue was extracted with 5% perchloric acid for 15 minutes at 90°. This extract was used for the estimation of DNA as phosphorus [10] and as deoxyribose by the diphenylamine reaction [4]. The correlation between the data obtained by the 2 methods was 0.98. The extracts had an OD ratio 265 mμ: 235 mμ between 1.5 to 2.0 and the correlation between the nucleic acid values obtained by OD and by phosphorus was 0.96.

Thymidine and Uridine Incorporation
into DNA and RNA

Incorporation studies were carried out under aseptic conditions. Seeds were surface sterilized with 1% sodium hypochlorite (Chlorox 1:5) for 20 minutes, rinsed 10 times with sterile water, then germinated and incubated under sterile conditions. Samples of incubation media, plated at the end of the incubation period on agar, did not show any contamination.

Seedlings were incubated as described above with thymidine-2-^{14}C (Schwarz Bioresearch Incorporated). One μc of the labeled compound was added to a flask containing 5 seedlings in 8 ml of solution. At the end of the incubation period the seedlings were rinsed, the epicotyl parts excised and extracted in a hand glass homogenizer by the procedure described above. The extraction buffer contained DNA, RNA and thymidine or uridine carrier, 200 μg/ml each. The radioactivity in the DNA and RNA extracts was determined with a Packard automatic Tri-Carb scintillation spectrometer, using 0.1 ml sample solution in 5 ml of scintillation solution according to Bray [1].

Extraction and Fractionation of
Thymidine-Labeled Nucleic Acids

Seedlings were incubated with tritiated thymidine (nominally 6-T, Nuclear Chicago). At the end of the incubation period the rinsed, excised epicotyls were extracted by the method of Ingle et al. [7], using a mortar and pestle. The final nucleic acid precipitate was dissolved in 20 ml of 0.4 M NaCl–0.05 M phosphate buffer pH 6.7 and forced into a MAK column prepared as described by Mandell and Hershey [11]. The column, containing the extract, was washed with 100 ml 0.4 M NaCl buffered solution. This was followed by elution with a linear gradient of 0.4 M (270 ml) to 1.2 M (270 ml) NaCl containing 0.05 M phosphate pH 6.7. The OD, at 260 mμ, of the 3 ml fractions was read in a Beckman (model DU) spectrophotometer. Radioactivity was determined with a Packard scintillation spectrometer as described above. Under these conditions there was no quenching due to salt.

Results

Lentil seedlings were incubated, after a 48-hour germination period, in the following incubation media: 1) control; standard medium, 2) 100 mg/liter GA$_3$, 3) 10^{-5} M FUDR, 4) 100 mg/liter GA$_3$ + 10^{-5} M FUDR. After an incubation period of another 48 hours in the dark, 250 to 300 epicotyls from each treatment were excised, weighed and extracted for

DNA and RNA determinations. The same procedure was carried out with seedlings at the initial state (see Materials and Methods). Ten seedlings were taken for length measurements and cell counts.

Cell Counts

Table 1 shows that the number of cells per epicotyl does not increase during the 48-hour incubation period. In fact, the number of cells per

TABLE 1

DNA and RNA Content of Lentil Epicotyls at the Initial State and After 48 Hours of Incubation With and Without GA, in the Presence and Absence of FUDR

Treatment	Length Mm/ Epicot.*	Fr Wt Mg/ Epicot.	DNA μg/ Epicot.	RNA μg/ Epicot.	Cell no. Thou- sands/ Epicot.	DNA μμg/Cell	RNA μμg/Cell
Initial state**	5.5	5.0	2.45	13.2	199	12.3	66.5
After 48 hr:							
Control	19.0	14.9	2.80	11.9	172	16.3	69.2
GA 100 mg/liter	27.6	29.4	3.74	15.4	170	22.0	90.9
FUDR, 10^{-5} M	10.9	12.0	2.20	11.2	180	12.2	62.1
GA + FUDR	16.9	20.0	2.96	11.9	167	17.7	71.3
S.E.	±0.5	±0.4	+0.15	±0.6	±9		

* Epicot. = epicotyl
** See Materials and Methods

epicotyl showed a slight but consistent decrease during the 48-hour incubation period, probably due to differentiation of vessels in the vascular tissue which is associated with the loss of individual cells. GA or FUDR do not seem to affect the cell number. These results clearly indicate that we are dealing here with a tissue of nondividing cells. This fully confirms our previous results, obtained by longitudinal sectioning of this tissue [12].

Net Determinations of DNA and RNA

Table 1 shows that during the incubation period of this experiment the epicotyls elongate from 5.5 mm to 27.6 mm with GA, as compared to 19.0 mm without GA. This elongation is inhibited by FUDR. It is also evident that the amount of DNA per epicotyl increases during the incubation period from 2.45 to 3.74 μg per epicotyl in the GA-treated seedlings. The increase under control conditions is much less. DNA synthesis in the elongating cells of the epicotyl is inhibited by FUDR in both cases. The amount of RNA per epicotyl is increased by the GA treatment. This promoted RNA synthesis is inhibited by FUDR. On a per cell basis, the amount of DNA increases from 12.3 μμg at the initial state to 16.3 μμg

without GA and 22.0 $\mu\mu$g DNA with a GA treatment. At the same time
the amount of RNA increases from 66.5 to 90.9 $\mu\mu$g RNA per cell with GA
while in the untreated and FUDR-inhibited cells the amount of RNA per
cell stays approximately at the initial level.

Incorporation of Thymidine and Uridine into DNA and RNA

Sterile lentil seedlings were incubated for 24 and 48 hours in flasks under
aseptic conditions, in the dark. Each flask contained 5 seedlings, 8 ml
standard incubation solution containing 1 μc of thymidine-^{14}C and 10^{-14} M
carrier thymidine plus the following: 1) control, 2) 100 mg/liter GA$_3$,
3) 10^{-5} M FUDR, 4) 100 mg/liter GA$_3$ + 10^{-5} M FUDR. Thymidine at a
concentration of 10^{-4} M completely reversed the inhibitory effect of 10^{-5} M
FUDR on elongation [12]. Under these conditions it could be expected
that DNA synthesis would not be inhibited by FUDR. Since, however,
FUDR inhibits the endogenous synthesis of thymidine, this compound
should promote the uptake and utilization of exogenous thymidine.

Table 2 shows that thymidine is incorporated into the DNA of the

TABLE 2

Incorporation of Thymidine-^{14}C into DNA and RNA of Lentil Epicotyls Incubated for 24 and
48 Hours With and Without GA, in the Presence and Absence of FUDR

All incubation media contained 10^{-4} M thymidine.

| Treatment | Fr Wt Mg/Epicot. | | Thymidine Uptake Cpm/Mg | | Incorporation of Thymidine into | | | |
| | | | | | DNA Cpm/Epicot. | | RNA Cpm/Epicot. | |
	24 hr	48 hr	24 hr	48 hr	24 hr	48 hr	24 hr	48 hr
Control	14.4	21.8	65	114	436	851	75	105
GA$_3$, 100 mg/liter	19.0	31.0	77	110	925	1081	67	75
FUDR, 10^{-5} M	13.4	19.8	100	123	716	1107	73	69
GA$_3$ + FUDR	16.4	40.6	117	147	1102	1890	73	128

elongating epicotyl cells whereas only a small fraction (6–10%) is incorporated into RNA. Moreover, the apparent incorporation into RNA
may be partly due to contamination of the RNA fraction with DNA. It
can be further seen that treatment of the seedlings with GA enhanced
the incorporation of thymidine into DNA. Total uptake of thymidine by
the tissue, measured by cpm per mg fresh weight, was increased either
only slightly, or not affected at all, by the GA treatment.

In a similar experiment the incorporation of uridine-^{14}C into RNA and
DNA of the lentil epicotyl was studied. The conditions of the experiment
were the same except that labeled uridine and 10^{-4} M uridine carrier were

TABLE 3

Incorporation of Uridine-^{14}C into DNA and RNA of Lentil Epicotyls Incubated
for 48 Hours With and Without GA

Incubation media contained 10^{-4} M uridine.

| | | | Incorporation of Uridine into | |
	Fr Wt Mg/Epicot.	Uridine Uptake Cpm/Mg	DNA Cpm/Epicot.	RNA Cpm/Epicot.
Control	22.6	236	315	2177
GA$_3$, 100 mg/liter	33.6	215	437	2966

used in place of thymidine. The incubation period was 48 hours and
FUDR was not used. Table 3 shows that uridine was incorporated mainly
into the RNA of the elongating epicotyl cells and that presence of GA
during incubation brought about a 36% increase in uridine incorporation
into RNA while the uptake of uridine was affected, if at all, very slightly
and moreover in the opposite direction. Uridine incorporation into DNA,
presumably after conversion into thymidine, was also increased by 38%,
but the counts in DNA (ca. 14% of counts in RNA) may, at least partially, result from a contamination of the DNA fraction with RNA.

Extraction and Fractionation of
Thymidine-Labeled Nucleic Acids

Seventy-five seedlings were incubated for 24 hours in a standard medium containing 10^{-4} M thymidine + 10^{-5} M FUDR. Fifteen additional
seedlings were incubated under aseptic conditions in a separate flask containing 30 ml of the same incubation medium plus 100 μc of thymidine-^{3}H.
Another batch of 75 + 15 seedlings was incubated under the same conditions but with the addition of 100 mg/liter ($=2.5 \times 10^{-4}$ M) GA. In either
case, the 90 epicotyls were extracted together, at the end of the incubation
period, and fractionated on a MAK column (see Materials and Methods).
Figure 1 shows that thymidine was heavily incorporated into the DNA
fraction. Neither the light nor the heavy ribosomal RNA fractions incorporated any significant amount of thymidine. Digestion of the extract with
ribonuclease, prior to fractionation on the MAK column, resulted in disappearance of the RNA peaks but had no effect on the DNA peak. GA-
treated epicotyls incorporated twice as much thymidine into the DNA as
did untreated controls. Table 4 shows that this increase in thymidine incorporation into DNA is not associated with any effect of GA on thymidine uptake. The DNA content per epicotyl as well as the specific activity
of the DNA are also larger in the GA-treated seedlings. Ribosomal RNA

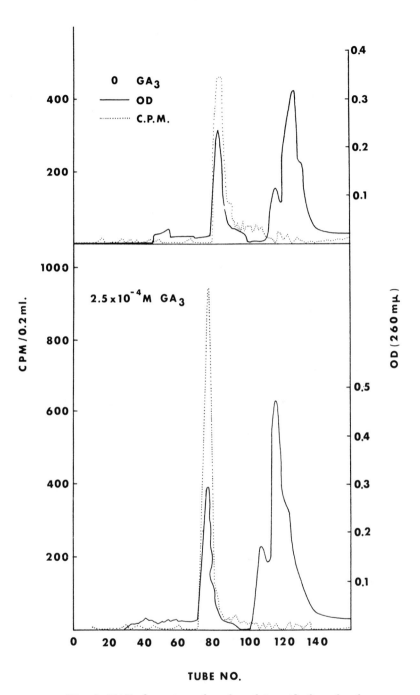

Fig. 1. MAK chromatography of nucleic acids from lentil epicotyls incubated for 24 hours with thymidine-^{3}H (100 μc/30 ml) in the presence and absence of 100 mg/liter GA$_3$. The incubation media contained 10^{-4} M thymidine carrier and 10^{-5} M FUDR. Column was eluted with a linear gradient of 0.4 M (270 ml) to 1.2 M (270 ml) NaCl containing 0.05 M phosphate pH 6.7. For further details see text.

TABLE 4

Incorporation of Thymidine-^{3}H into the MAK Column-DNA Fraction of Lentil Epicotyls Incubated for 24 Hours With and Without GA

Incubation media contained 10^{-4} M thymidine and 10^{-5} M FUDR

	Fr Wt Mg/ Epicot.	Thymidine Uptake Cpm/Mg	Incorpora-tion into DNA Cpm/ Epicot.	DNA Con-tent OD/ Epicot.	Specific Activity Cpm $\times$ 10^{-3} per OD	Ribosomal RNA Con-tent OD/ Epicot.
Control	12.9	1126	2371	0.039	60.8	0.135
GA$_3$, 100 mg/liter	19.2	1073	4001	0.049	81.6	0.191

content per epicotyl in the GA-treated seedlings is increased by 41% as compared to GA-free controls.

Discussion

Our experiments have been concerned with synthesis of DNA during growth of the lentil epicotyl, an organ growing only by cell elongation, and with the effects of GA and FUDR on this process. Some determinations of RNA synthesis have also been made.

The following 3 points are important for the interpretation of the results: A) The specificity of thymidine incorporation into the DNA fraction and of uridine incorporation into the RNA fraction of the tissue (tables 2, 3) indicate that these fractions are genuine. This is further strengthened by the exclusive incorporation of thymidine into the MAK-column DNA fraction, with no significant incorporation into any of the other nucleic-acid fractions of the tissue.

B) The differences in DNA and RNA synthesis in tissues treated and not treated with GA and/or FUDR, as measured by thymidine or uridine incorporation, cannot be explained by differences in the uptake of the precursors into the tissue since these latter differences were always considerably smaller than those in incorporation.

C) The number of cells per epicotyl being fairly constant, the data, presented throughout this paper on a per-epicotyl basis (transformed to a per-cell basis in table 1 only), express in fact DNA content per cell and its changes. The average amount of DNA in a lentil epicotyl cell, determined in this way, compares closely with the amounts reported by Rasch et al. [14] who found 18 $\mu\mu$g DNA per diploid nucleus of bean plant cells. (It may be noted that the uptake of thymidine and of uridine in tables 2, 3 and 4 is expressed on a fresh-weight rather than a per-epicotyl basis. This is justified since incorporation of a metabolite into cell constituents will depend on its concentration, rather than its total amount, in the cell.)

Our results reveal the following 3 features of the elongating cells of the lentil epicotyl: 1) The cells are synthesizing DNA while they elongate; 2) presence of exogenous GA, which enhances elongation, also enhances DNA synthesis during this process. DNA synthesis takes place also during a "gibberellinless" elongation. The existence of endogenous gibberellins in dark-grown pea seedlings [9] suggests however that GA participates also in the basal growth of the lentil epicotyl; 3) FUDR, which inhibits elongation [see also 12], inhibits DNA synthesis in these cells. Thymidine incorporation into the DNA of the cells is increased however when FUDR is applied with a sufficient amount of exogenous thymidine (table 2). This is to be expected if FUDR acts by inhibiting thymidine synthesis in the tissue since depletion of the endogenous thymidine pool will result in increased utilization of exogenously supplied thymidine.

Our results pose quite a number of questions, some of which can be answered at least in a tentative manner while others will require further experimental work.

A) Are the DNA contents of the cells found after incubation determined only by DNA synthesis, or is turnover of DNA also a factor? Some idea of this problem can be obtained by comparison of the data in tables 1 and 2. If the cpm incorporated into the DNA of the tissue, namely, 1890 and 1107 cpm in 48 hours, with and without GA, respectively, are transformed to μg of thymidine (the specific activity of thymidine in the incubation medium was 7617 cpm per μg) and these in turn into μg of DNA the resulting values are 1.34 μg and 0.78 μg DNA per epicotyl, respectively. The direct determinations of DNA in the tissue (table 1) gave values of 1.29 μg and 0.35 μg of net DNA increase, respectively. This comparison indicates that DNA synthesis accounts for a substantial part of the thymidine incorporation data, but it also suggests that some DNA turnover took place in the cells, particularly in absence of exogenous GA.

B) Does the increase in DNA content per cell during elongation, whether with or without exogenous GA, represent an increase in nuclear or cytoplasmic DNA, or both? The amount of cytoplasmic DNA in a tissue like that used in our determinations, grown and incubated in the dark and therefore not containing fully developed chloroplasts, is probably not more than 1% of nuclear DNA [6]. Therefore, it seems highly probable that an increase in DNA content of between 16% and 50% (table 1) is based on an increase in nuclear (or both nuclear and cytoplasmic) DNA.

C) What is the relation between DNA synthesis and cell elongation? Some information bearing on this point has been discussed previously [12]. The finding that cell elongation in the lentil epicotyl is accompanied by substantial, readily measurable increases in both content and synthesis rates of DNA in the cells permits some additional conclusions. Two major possibilities of the significance of DNA synthesis for cell elongation may be visualized. Firstly, it may be assumed that the process of DNA synthesis itself does not play any specific role in cell elongation, and that it is only its result, that is the increased DNA content in the cells, which is important. Substantial increases of the DNA content have long been known to occur in elongating and differentiating plant cells, as the phenomena of polyploidy and polyteny. However, there is presently no evidence that these phenomena are essential for the growth and differentiation of plant cells (see Discussion in [5], p 107–09). On the other hand it is possible that only a small fraction of cellular DNA is essential for cell elongation and that only the increase in this specific fraction is important.

Secondly, it may be assumed that some genes have to duplicate or "turn over" in order to produce their characteristic RNA which in turn would be essential for elongation of the cell. In lentil epicotyls incubated in the presence of GA, and exhibiting increased elongation, RNA synthesis was promoted along with DNA synthesis: by 31% by net determination (table 1), and 36% by uridine incorporation (table 2). Table 4 shows that this increase may be accounted for by an increase in ribosomal RNA (41% above the GA-free control). This GA-induced synthesis of ribosomal RNA was inhibited by FUDR (table 1), that is, it was apparently dependent on DNA synthesis. In this connection, it may be of interest that the nucleolus has been confirmed as the site of synthesis of ribosomal RNA [2, 14] and the nucleolar organizer segment of the chromosomes was identified as the DNA template for this process [14]. It was also shown that inhibition of DNA synthesis by an overdose of thymidine resulted in a block of uridine incorporation into nucleolar and cytoplasmic RNA but not into nuclear RNA [8]. This seems in agreement with our results, and it seems possible that continuous DNA synthesis is needed for the production of ribosomal RNA, and that the latter is in turn needed for cell elongation in some plant tissues.

By which mechanism presence of GA results in an enhancement of DNA synthesis is entirely unknown and is a question that requires much further investigation. The results reported in this paper provide additional and direct evidence for the earlier conclusion [12] that elongation in certain plant cells is dependent on DNA synthesis.

Literature Cited

1. Bray, G. A. 1960. A simple efficient liquid scintillator for counting aqueous solutions in a liquid scintillation counter. Anal. Biochem. 1: 279–85.

2. Brown, D. D. and J. B. Gurdon. 1964. Absence of ribosomal RNA synthesis in the anucleolate mutant of *Xenopus laevis*. Proc. Natl. Acad. Sci. 51: 139–46.

3. Brown, R. and P. Rickless. 1949. A new method for the study of cell division and cell extension with some preliminary observations on the effect of temperature and of nutrients. Proc. Roy. Soc. (London) Ser. B. 136: 110–25.

4. Burton, K. 1956. A study of the conditions and mechanisms of the diphenylamine reaction for the colorimetric estimation of DNA. Biochem. J. 62: 315–23.

5. Buvat, R. 1965. Les bases cytologiques de la différenciation et de la dédifférenciation chez les plantes. In: Encyclopedia of Plant Physiology, Vol. XV/1. Springer-Verlag, Berlin. p 100–45.

6. Gibor, A. and S. Granick. 1964. Plastids and mitochondria; inheritable systems. Science 145: 890–97.

7. Ingle, J., J. L. Key, and R. E. Holm. 1965. Demonstration and characterization of a DNA-like RNA in excised plant tissue. J. Mol. Biol. 11: 730–46.

8. Kasten, F. H., F. F. Strasser, and M. Turner. 1965. Nucleolar and cytoplasmic ribonucleic acid inhibition by excess thymidine. Nature 207: 161–64.

9. Kende, H. and A. Lang. 1964. Gibberellins and light inhibition of stem growth in peas. Plant Physiol. 39: 435–40.

10. King, E. J. 1932. The colorimetric determination of phosphorus. Determination of total phosphorus. Biochem. J. 26: 292–97.

11. Mandell, J. D. and A. D. Hershey. 1960. A fractionating column for analysis of nucleic acids. Anal. Biochem. 1: 66–77.

12. Nitsan, J. and A. Lang. 1965. Inhibition of cell division and cell elongation in higher plants by inhibitors of DNA synthesis. Develop. Biol. 12: 358–76.

13. Rasch, E., H. Swift, and R. M. Klein. 1959. Nucleoprotein changes in plant-tumor growth. J. Biophys. Biochem. Cytol. 6: 11–34.

14. Ritossa, F. M. and S. Spiegelman. 1965. Localization of DNA complementary to ribosomal RNA in the nucleolus organizer region of *Drosophila melanogaster*. Proc. Natl. Acad. Sci. 53: 737–45.

15. Smillie, R. M. and G. Krotkov. 1960. The estimation of nucleic acids in some algae and higher plants. Can. J. Botany 38: 31–49.

Hormonal Control of Enzyme Synthesis in Barley Endosperm

J. E. Varner
G. Ram Chandra

The activities of several enzymes of isolated barley endosperm increase markedly in response to added gibberellic acid [1–6]. In the normal, intact germinating seed, evocation of these same enzymatic activities in the endosperm is caused by the embryo which is known to produce gibberellic acid [7, 8]. We have, in the present case then, an example of hormonally regulated enzymatic activity and one with which it is particularly convenient to work since the principle enzyme involved is α-amylase. We shall show below that the gibberellic acid-dependent increase in α-amylase activity in barley endosperm is due to *de novo* synthesis of the enzyme. Thus, when isolated barley endosperm is treated with gibberellic acid in the presence of C^{14}-labeled amino acids and the α-amylase subsequently isolated, it is found to contain label.

We shall further show that the α-amylase produced in response to application of gibberellic acid is identical with that synthesized by the normally germinating seedling. Finally, we shall show that the gibberellic acid-induced synthesis of α-amylase is suppressed in the presence of actinomycin D, and that the effect of gibberellic acid is therefore upon the expression of the genetic information which controls α-amylase production.

Materials and Methods

Dry barley seeds (*Hordeum vulgare,* var. Himalaya) were cut in half along their equatorial axes and the embryo halves discarded. The endosperm halves were soaked in 1% sodium hypochlorite for 15–20 min, rinsed in sterile distilled water, and transferred aseptically to sterile moist sand contained in Petri dishes. After incubation for 3 days at 17–23°, ten half-seeds were transferred to an aseptic 25-ml Erlenmeyer flask containing 2.0 ml of 0.001 M sodium acetate buffer (pH 4.8) and the appropriate treatment solution. Such flasks were shaken at top speed at 25° on a Dubnoff metabolic shaker during the incubation period. The medium was then poured off, and the half-seeds were rinsed once with 3.0 ml distilled water. They were next ground in a mortar with sand and 5.0 ml 0.001 M acetate buffer (pH 4.8). The homogenate was then centrifuged at 1000 × g. The resultant supernatant (extract) and the incubation medium

Reprinted by permission of the authors and publisher from *Proceedings of the National Academy of Science, 52:* 100–106, 1964. This research was supported by research contract AT (30–1)–3232 with the Atomic Energy Commission.

were next assayed separately for α-amylase activity by the method of Shuster and Gifford [9]. The assay was calibrated by use of crystalline α-amylase prepared according to Schwimmer and Balls [10].

Labeled, gibberellic acid-induced α-amylase for fingerprinting was prepared as follows: twenty preincubated half-seeds were aseptically transferred to an aseptic 25-ml Erlenmeyer flask which contained 1.0 ml of 0.001 M acetate buffer (pH 4.8), 10^{-6} M gibberellic acid, and 20 μc of L-threonine-C^{14}. After 24 hr incubation at 25°, the medium contained 400 μg of α-amylase. The medium was poured off, and the half-seeds were rinsed twice with 1.0-ml portions of water. Authentic carrier α-amylase (4.5 mg) was added to the combined medium and washings.

Calcium chloride was added to a final concentration of 0.003 M and the solution adjusted to pH 7.0. The solution was then heated at 70° for 20 min, centrifuged, and the precipitate discarded. Carrier L-threonine (0.01 M) was added and enough absolute alcohol added to make the solution 40% with respect to ethanol. After 10 min the solution was centrifuged and the precipitate discarded. Glycogen (0.2 ml of a 1.6% solution [11]) was added and after 10 min the precipitate recovered by centrifugation. The glycogen-α-amylase precipitate was washed once with 2.0 ml of 40% ethanol and taken up in 1.0 ml of H_2O. The solution of the glycogen-α-amylase complex was incubated at 25° for 1 hr to digest the glycogen then dialyzed overnight against 0.01 M L-threonine.

The labeled α-amylase preparation was heated to 95° for 5 min and ammonium carbonate added to a final concentration of 0.01 M, and incubated at 20° for 18 hr with 20 μg of trypsin. After freeze-drying and sublimation of the ammonium carbonate, the hydrolysate was separated into its component peptides by chromatography and electrophoresis [14].

The α-amylase is produced by the aleurone layer of the seed. Dissection of half-seeds into aleurone layers (plus testa-pericarp) and starchy endosperm was performed after the 3-day preincubation period.

Labeled amino acids (L-threonine-u-C^{14} and L-phenylalanine-u-C^{14}) were purchased from the New England Nuclear Corporation, Boston. The actinomycin D was a gift from Dr. Clement A. Stone of the Merck Institute for Therapeutic Research, West Point, Pa. The 5-bromouracil, 6-azaguanine, and 8-azaadenine were purchased from California Corporation for Biochemical Research, Bethesda, Md.

Crystalline trypsin was obtained from the Worthington Biochemical Corporation, Freehold, N.J.

The rabbit liver glycogen was purchased from Nutritional Biochemicals, Cleveland, Ohio, and further purified as described by Loyter and Schramm [11]. Barley malt α-amylase for use as standard and carrier was purified and crystallized by the method of Loyter and Schramm [11] and of Schwimmer and Balls [10]. The two methods yielded α-amylase of identical specific (enzymatic) activities. The incorporation of labeled amino acids into protein was determined by addition to the extract of 10% trichloroacetic acid containing 0.01 M carrier amino acid. The precipitate was filtered on a membrane filter (Schleicher and Shuell, B-6) and washed with 10% trichloroacetic acid. Radioactivity was measured with a Nuclear-Chicago gas-flow (D-47) detector.

Results

The time course of the development of α-amylase activity in half-seeds and in isolated aleurone layers in response to added gibberellic acid is given in Fig. 1. There is a lag period of 9–15 hr after addition of gib-

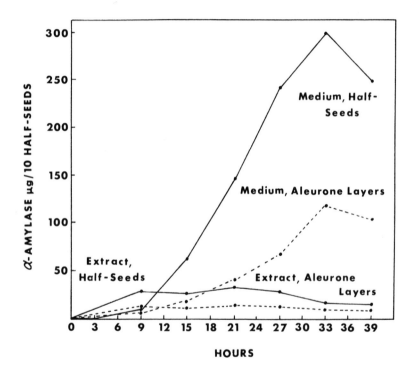

Fig. 1. Time course for the development of α-amylase activity in half-seeds and in isolated aleurone layers. The fresh weight of ten half-aleurone layers (plus testa-pericarp) is 168 mg. The gibberellic acid (10^{-6} M) was added at 0 time.

berellic acid before the maximum rate of production of α-amylase is attained. Production of the enzyme ceases suddenly about 33 hr after addition of the hormone. The bulk of the α-amylase produced is released into the medium surrounding the tissue. Although isolated aleurone layers do not produce as much α-amylase as intact half-seeds, we believe that this is a matter of nutrition. The addition of phosphate ions, calcium ions, magnesium ions and glucose, and amino acids increases the quantity of α-amylase produced by isolated aleurone layers.

It is clear that the aleurone cells are able to incorporate labeled amino acids into protein in the absence of added gibberellic acid (Table 1). This

TABLE 1

L-Phenylalanine-C^{14} Incorporation into Protein *in Vivo*

Hours		Minus Gibberellic Acid			Plus Gibberellic Acid		
		Radio-activity, in protein, cpm	% Labeled protein precipitated by heating	α-Amylase, μg	Radio-activity in protein, cpm	% Labeled protein precipitated by heating	α-Amylase, μg
10	Medium	16	0	3	41	0	19
	Extract	640	74	<20	480	79	28
20	Medium	92	2	7	287	37	276
	Extract	2200	75	<20	588	74	31
30	Medium	176	23	12	480	40	440
	Extract	2760	75	<20	465	76	15

Each flask contained ten half-seeds, 10^{-8} M acetate buffer, and 1.0 μc of L-phenylalanine-C^{14}. The counts shown were for 0.10-ml aliquots of a total of 5.0 ml.

fact, together with the knowledge that there is no increase in respiration preceding or paralleling α-amylase formation [12], and that there is no qualitative change in the pattern of $P^{32}O_4$ incorporation into acid-soluble compounds [12] following the addition of gibberellic acid, allows us to conclude that the energy apparatus and the materials for protein synthesis are at hand before the addition of gibberellic acid. It is, therefore, the function of gibberellic acid to influence the synthesis of certain specific proteins. A further examination of Table 1 shows that the total label of amino acid incorporated into protein decreased in half-seeds incubated with gibberellic acid. This is the result of a gibberellic acid-dependent increase in proteolytic activity [13] which causes the release within the tissue of relatively large quantities of free amino acids [4]. The increase in level of free amino acids in turn dilutes out the label added and makes it impossible to determine readily the amount of protein synthesized in the gibberellic acid-treated half-seeds. Inhibitors of protein synthesis prevent the gibberellic acid-induced increase in proteolytic activity [12]. It is, therefore, likely that the protease is also produced by *de novo* synthesis. For the present discussion, it is sufficient to observe (Table 1) the marked difference in the distribution of the labeled protein between medium and extract in the gibberellic acid-treated and -untreated half-seeds, and the rough parallel between the release of α-amylase into the medium and the release of labeled proteins into the medium. In the absence of gibberellic acid, about 5 per cent of the newly synthesized, i.e., labeled, protein is released into the medium during a 30-hr incubation period. In the presence of gibberellic acid, about 50 per cent of the newly synthesized protein· is released into the medium.

The physical properties of the labeled proteins formed undergo a dramatic qualitative transformation in the presence of gibberellic acid (Table 1). Of the proteins labeled in the absence of gibberellic acid, about 75 per cent are precipitated by heating to 70° for 20 min. Only 0–40 per cent of the labeled proteins released into the medium in the presence of GA are thus precipitated (Table 1). Addition of carrier extract to the labeled medium does not carry down any more of the labeled proteins during the heating of the medium, nor does the medium stabilize the labeled proteins in the extract. It is, of course, well known that α-amylase is heat-stable. So also is the endo-β-glucanase which increases as does α-amylase in response to added gibberellic acid [4]. The α-amylase recovered by the ethanol-glycogen procedure [11] contains about 12 per cent of the total counts incorporated into protein and about 35 per cent of the heat-stable labeled proteins (Table 2). Thus, α-amylase accounts for a

TABLE 2

Physical Properties of Labeled Proteins

Fraction	Radioactivity, Cpm	Heat-Precipitable, %
Extract	34,000	80
Medium	29,200	15
Ethanol PPT	7,000	0
Glycogen S.F.	8,000	0
α-Amylase	8,000	0

The numbers shown indicate the total number of counts incorporated into protein during incubation of ten half-seeds in acetate buffer, 10^{-6} M gibberellic acid, and 1 μc of L-leucine-C^{14}. The ethanol precipitate, glycogen supernatant fraction, and α-amylase fraction refer to the fractions produced during the purification procedure [11].

large fraction of the total protein synthesis triggered by gibberellic acid.

Labeled leucine, alanine, proline, and threonine were all shown, in separate experiments, to be incorporated into the purified α-amylase. Each of these labeled samples of α-amylase was digested with trypsin and "fingerprinted" [14]. Of a total of 31 ninhydrin spots, 20 were labeled with proline, 26 with alanine, 30 with leucine, and 25 with threonine. Only 2 of the 31 ninhydrin spots contained none of the above labeled amino acids. The fingerprint obtained with labeled threonine is shown in Fig. 2.

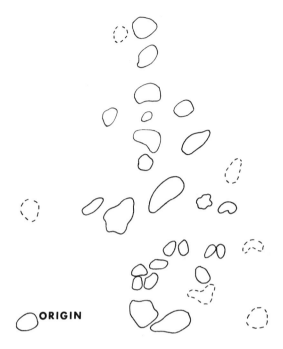

Fig. 2. Autoradiograph of a fingerprint of α-amylase obtained
by tryptic digestion of threonine-C[14] labeled α-amylase. The
solid lines show the position of ninhydrin-positive spots which
coincide with the exposed spot on the film. The dotted lines
are ninhydrin-positive spots which were not labeled.

We experienced some difficulty in obtaining complete digestion of the
α-amylase with trypsin. The rate of digestion is slow and variable. This is
probably due to the presence of limit dextrins and traces of calcium ions
which may serve to protect the α-amylase against tryptic attack. It appears from the information of Fig. 2 as well as from the similar finger-
prints of α-amylase labeled with other amino acids that the entire α-amylase molecule is synthesized in response to the addition of gibberellic acid.

We turn next to the question of how gibberellic acid causes the production of α-amylase. It could, in principle, be through derepression of
the previously repressed gene for α-amylase synthesis with consequent
production of appropriate messenger RNA. We approach this problem by
finding out whether inhibitors of RNA synthesis inhibit the gibberellic
acid-dependent synthesis of α-amylase.

Of the RNA synthesis inhibitors used, 5-bromouracil, 8-azaadenine, and
actinomycin D caused some inhibition of α-amylase formation (Table 3).
Application of 100 μg/ml of actinomycin D completely inhibits the formation of α-amylase (Table 3), although 10 μg/ml is almost without effect.
We suspect that actinomycin D is partially destroyed by the proteases of

TABLE 3

The Effect of RNA Synthesis Inhibitors on α-Amylase
Formation by Isolated Aleurone Layers

	α-Amylase, μg		
Treatment	Extract	Medium	Total
– GA	9.4	5.8	15.2
Control	12	53	65
5-Bromouracil	10	26	36
6-Azaguanine	14	43	57
8-Azaadenine	10	33	43
Actinomycin D	10	4.3	14.3

For each sample, ten half-aleurone layers were incubated with buffer, 10^{-6} M gibberellic acid, and 10^{-4} M
inhibitor—except the actinomycin D which was 100 $\mu g/$
ml—for 30 hrs at 25°.

barley because addition of 10^{-3} M potassium bromate (which inhibits the
protease action without preventing α-amylase synthesis) [12] to the medium together with gibberellic acid and actinomycin D increases the inhibition caused by 10–50 $\mu g/ml$ of actinomycin D. Evidence that actinomycin D, even at these high concentrations, is, in fact, selective is
shown in Table 4. In the presence of gibberellic acid and actinomycin D,
the small amount of α-amylase formed and the distribution of labeled proteins are characteristic of the untreated aleurone layers. However, actinomycin D has little effect on the rate of the gibberellic acid-independent
incorporation of labeled phenylalanine into proteins. The obvious and
most attractive conclusion is that the labeled heat-stable proteins syn-

TABLE 4

Amino Acid Incorporation in Vivo
by Aleurone Layers

Treatment		Radioactivity		α-Amylase, μg	
GA	Act D	Extract	Medium	Extract	Medium
–	–	72,600	18,900	22	11
+	–	21,300	25,500	12	55
–	+	69,900	12,700	4	0.5
+	+	74,000	18,000	26	12

The numbers shown indicate total c/m incorporated into
protein during a 30-hr incubation of ten half-aleurone
layers with buffer, 1 μc L-phenylalanine-C[14], 10^{-6} M gibberellic acid, and 100 $\mu g/ml$ actinomycin D where indicated.

thesized and released into the medium after the addition of gibberellic acid require DNA-dependent synthesis of RNA. That incorporation which occurs without added gibberellic acid could use messenger RNA formed during the preincubation period or perhaps even during the maturation of the developing seed.

The formation of α-amylase by the isolated aleurone layers is sensitive to actinomycin D only during the first few hours after addition of gibberellic acid (Table 5). Actinomycin D added 7 hr after the addition of

TABLE 5

Time Course of Sensitivity to Inhibitors

Conditions	α-Amylase, μg
−GA	13
+GA	66
+GA + Act D	24
+GA + Act D (after 7 hr)	55
+GA + pFφ Ala	12
+GA + pFφ Ala (after 7 hr)	12

For each sample, ten half-aleurone layers were incubated with buffer, and 10^{-6} M gibberellic acid added at the beginning of the incubation. The actinomycin D (100 μg/ml) and p-fluorophenylalanine (10^{-3} M) were added either at the same time as the gibberellic acid or after 7 hr.

gibberellic acid has little effect. However, p-fluorophenylalanine added at this time is still effective. These results are consistent with the postulate that the addition of gibberellic acid causes the formation of a specific messenger RNA which directs the *de novo* synthesis of α-amylase. Within a few hours after the addition of gibberellic acid, the quantity of messenger RNA is no longer rate-limiting in α-amylase synthesis. From this time on, the formation of α-amylase would not be susceptible to inhibition by actinomycin D but would, of course, still be susceptible to protein synthesis inhibitors.

Discussion

Simple dissection experiments have shown that only the aleurone layer cells are capable of respiration and amino acid incorporation [6]. The QO_2 ($\mu l \cdot O_2 \cdot hr^{-1} \cdot 100$ mg fresh wt^{-1}) for the aleurone layers at 25° is 15–30. The aleurone layers consist of a single cell type derived from the triple fusion nucleus. Aside from the possibility that a layer of living cells surrounding the dead starchy endosperm may provide protection against attack by microorganisms, the only obvious function of the aleurone cells is to produce and secrete hydrolytic enzymes for the digestion of the reserves of the dead starchy endosperm cells. It is a delightful nicety that the key to these reserves is kept by the embryo—the only tissue capable of growth. The simplest possible way to explain the data in this paper is to postulate that gibberellic acid exerts its control at the level of the gene to bring about the synthesis of messenger RNA's specific for the proteins being synthesized. It appears that this hypothesis can be checked experimentally by the techniques developed for assessing those DNA sites available in chromatin for transcription into messenger RNA by RNA polymerase [15].

Summary

The development of α-amylase activity by isolated aleurone layers of barley endosperm is completely dependent upon added gibberellic acid and is a result of the *de novo* synthesis of the α-amylase molecule. The synthesis of α-amylase and of other heat-stable proteins is prevented by actinomycin D. It is therefore postulated that gibberellic acid controls the synthesis of α-amylase and of other heat-stable proteins in aleurone cells by causing the production of specific messenger RNA's.

1. Yomo, H., and H. Iinuma, *Agri. Biol. Chem.* (*Tokyo*), **26**, 201 (1962).

2. Paleg, L., *Plant Physiol.*, **36**, 829 (1961).

3. MacLeod, A. M., and A. S. Millar, *J. Inst. Brewing*, **68**, 322 (1962).

4. Briggs, D. E., *J. Inst. Brewing*, **69**, 13 (1963).

5. Varner, J. E., and G. Schidlovsky, in *Proceedings of the International Seed Protein Conference*, New Orleans, USDA (1963).

6. Varner, J. E., *Plant Physiol.*, **39**, 413 (1964).

7. Yomo, H., *Hakko Kyokaishi*, **18**, 603 (1960).

8. Paleg, L. G., *Plant Physiol.*, **35**, 902 (1960).

9. Shuster, L., and R. H. Gifford. *Arch. Biochem. Biophys.*, **96**, 534 (1962).

10. Schwimmer, S., and A. K. Balls, *J. Biol. Chem.*, **179**, 1063 (1949).

11. Loyter, A., and M. Schramm, *Biochim. Biophys. Acta*, **65**, 200 (1962).

12. Ram Chandra, G., and J. E. Varner, unpublished.

13. Yomo, H., *Hakko Kyokaishi*, **19**, 284 (1961); *Chem. Abstracts*, **57**, 11544 (1961).

14. Katz, A. M., W. J. Dreyer, and C. B. Anfinsen, *J. Biol. Chem.*, **234**, 2897 (1959).

15. Bonner, J., R. C. Huang, and R. O. Gilden, these PROCEEDINGS, **50**, 793 (1963).

3 / Cytokinins

The one paper in these readings that may be said to be a classic in the accepted sense of that term is the initial work in this section, by Skoog and Miller. Their demonstration that a third class of plant growth regulators, the cytokinins, interact with auxins to regulate differentiation has profoundly affected the thinking of plant as well as animal biologists. These investigators were able to switch undifferentiated cells into one or another pathway of differentiation simply by varying ratios of two growth hormones supplied to plant tissue cultures. Thus either root or shoot formation could be obtained at will from given tissue. A more remarkable illustration of the molecular control of growth processes is difficult to visualize.

One measure of the importance of a research report is the amount of new work it stimulates in the same or related fields. On that basis the second reading in this section has few peers among plant growth substance papers. The observation was a simple one: detached leaves treated with cytokinins remained green and metabolically healthy much longer than controls. The significance of this effect was far reaching, however, since it implicated the cytokinins in the control of protein synthesis, a conclusion that did not escape the authors, Richmond and Lang.

Further evidence for this role of the cytokinins came quickly from a number of laboratories. Particularly brilliant has been the research of Mothes and his colleagues, who, in a series of papers, have demonstrated the important part played by cytokinins in the mobilization of low molecular weight precursors to protein synthesis. The third reading here is one of the few English-language papers by this group and will give the reader a good idea of the direction this important line of work is taking.

The ultimate paper in this section was the first of a rapidly increasing list of reports that suggest that the cytokinins are directly involved in RNA metabolism.

Chemical Regulation of Growth and Organ Formation in Plant Tissues Cultured *in Vitro*

Folke Skoog
Carlos O. Miller

I. Introduction

In the context of the symposium this report is to deal with the biological action of growth substances as revealed in organ formation, especially bud formation in plant tissues cultured *in vitro*. This emphasis on technique may give the impression that we are dealing with a concise, rigidly defined subject, perhaps even too technical and artificial to be of general biological interest or usefulness. Actually the problems of growth encountered in studies of tissue and organ cultures are essentially as complex as in those of intact organisms, but a brief consideration of the experimental approach itself as well as of the results is called for. The vast domain of morphogenesis has been explored for a long time from different points of view and staked out into separate fields of highly specialized disciplines. Each of these which has been intensively studied has yielded its share of information for the development of such general concepts and understanding of growth as we now have.

The "Formal" Biochemical Approach

In dealing with biochemical aspects of morphogenesis, Needham has distinguished between (1) morphogenetic substratum, (2) morphogenetic stimuli and (3) morphogenetic mechanisms. The validity of such categories, especially the existence of the third as set apart from the first two, is debatable; and if this third category is at all logically justifiable, it must be as a very temporary scaffold for the elaboration of the others. Nevertheless, arbitrary as this classification may be, these first two categories at least serve to draw attention to distinctions between problems of raw materials and energy supplies for growth on the one hand, and the finer regulation of rates and co-ordination of component processes on the other. At the present time major emphasis seems to be on aspects of the former of these categories, i.e. metabolism. Especially intermediary carbohydrate metabolism is being studied extensively and scrutinized intensively for possible clues to the secret of growth. From this line of approach come

Reprinted by permission of the authors and publisher from *Symposia of the Society for Experimental Biology, 11*: 118–131, 1957. Much of the work covered in this report was supported in part by the University of Wisconsin Research Committee of the Graduate School with funds from the Alumni Research Foundation and by a research grant (Proj. BO-19 to F. Skoog) from the American Cancer Society upon recommendation of the Committee on Growth of the National Research Council.

reports in which differences between normal development and uncontrolled growth of cancer are considered as being due merely to the funnelling of the energy-providing substrate into alternative aerobic or anaerobic, that is, respiratory, fermentative or otherwise grossly different pathways of degradation. Somewhat more subtle and now extremely popular are working hypotheses based on the assumption that the relative quantitative activities of key enzyme systems in the general respiratory chain are decisive in the regulation of growth. When it is considered, however, that complete cessation of growth may be achieved, at least in plants, by lowering the total respiratory rate by as little as 10–20% through the intervention of various inhibitors, it would appear that the energy-supplying mechanism as such, although it is a prerequisite for growth, can hardly act as a sensitive governor of the processes involved in normal differentiation and development. It seems rather that biochemistry in its preoccupation with metabolic cycles has revealed the general nature of the energy-furnishing machinery but not yet the finer points of its operation. This is said, not to detract from the great achievements in this field, but to emphasize the necessity, in analyses of growth, of working also at higher levels of structural organization, i.e. of using more complex systems than it has been possible to handle effectively so far with chemical tools exclusively.

The Physiological Approach with Plants

(a) *General physiological analyses.* From the more physiological approach to the analysis of growth, students of plants early postulated separate factors for the regulation of successive phases of development. Sachs spoke of specific organ-forming substances. At the cellular level a sharp distinction was made between increase in size and numbers. Much effort has been spent in studies of cell elongation and cell division as processes separate and distinct from one another, and in attempts to determine the additive contributions and interactions of the two in tissue differentiation and in organ formation, especially as observed in regeneration phenomena.

(b) *Search for growth hormones.* A natural consequence of this reasoning has been a deliberate search for a specific chemical regulator of cell elongation and a specific regulator of cell division as well as, of course, the continuing search for specific organ-forming substances. It is said that he who seeks shall find. We now have the auxins, the very definition of which is based on physiological activity (hormone action) leading to cell enlargement. Also for a long time there has been good indirect evidence for a cell-division hormone (Haberlandt, 1921), and recently the term kinin has been proposed as a generic name for substances with physiological activity promoting cell division in plant tissues under certain specified conditions (Miller, Skoog, Okumura, von Saltza & Strong, 1956; Strong,

Okumura, von Saltza, Miller & Skoog, unpublished). Further investigations into the manner in which the known growth regulators exert their specific effects in cell elongation and division respectively have led to a blank wall. Instead of finding their intimate and unique nature, we have found that they are involved indirectly in a wide variety of biochemical activities or physiological functions and lead to most heterogeneous histological and morphological end-results. For example, under appropriate conditions auxins have been shown on the one hand to promote root formation and even cell division in the cambium (Snow, 1935); and, on the other hand, to inhibit root elongation and bud development. Thus we do not yet know the specific organ-forming substances, but instead evidence is accumulating against their existence; although various claims and specifications for calines (in the sense of Went's proposal, 1951), for rhizocaline (Bouillenne, 1950), florigens, vernalins, etc., are still being made.

(c) In vitro *studies of nutrient and growth-factor relationships.* The complexity and variability in growth responses indicated above obviously mean that the interaction of many factors must be considered, and that some of these perhaps might be revealed in studies of the simplest possible material capable of "multiple growth responses" and grown under as rigidly standardized conditions as reasonably could be attained. The present experimental approach utilizing stem segments, pith and callus tissues grown on inorganic nutrient media with added organic substrates and various growth factors was intended to eliminate some of the extraneous features and variables which are difficult to control in intact plants. Because valid comparisons and integration of results obtained with different tissue-culture methods and materials are still very difficult, if not impossible, the present discussion will be confined mainly to work carried out in our laboratory, with only brief consideration given to pertinent work in other laboratories. Details of the methodology, media, etc., have been reported (Skoog & Tsui, 1948; Miller & Skoog, 1953; Jablonski & Skoog, 1954). It is hoped that the evidence to be presented will convincingly demonstrate that this approach does in fact permit a closer examination of individual factors and their interaction in various growth processes than has been possible so far with intact plants. For a more general review of the tissue-culture approach in studies of growth see Gautheret (1955).

II. General Results

The present work was started in an attempt to account for the dual, stimulatory and inhibitory, action of auxin (IAA) as exemplified in its promotion of growth of the terminal shoot and inhibition of lateral buds. A study particularly of the latter process led to the recognition of a parallel function of auxin in the initial formation of organ primordia and in the subsequent development of buds.

Interaction of IAA, Adenine and Other Factors in Bud Formation

Experiments with tobacco callus and stem tissues cultured *in vitro* have shown that a delicate, quantitative balance between IAA and adenine and between these and other factors will determine the types of growth and organ formation which occur (Skoog & Tsui, 1951; Miller & Skoog, 1953; Skoog, 1954*a*). For example, with reference to the induction of bud formation in tobacco-stem segment cultures, the addition of 5 μg./l. IAA to the medium was enough to prevent completely spontaneous bud formation in control segments, and about 40 mg. of adenine must be supplied to restore bud formation to the same level as in controls. Computations on the basis of numerous experiments of this type indicated that under the conditions used about 15,000 molecules of adenine were required to counterbalance 1 molecule of IAA. Furthermore, by the use of purine-type inhibitors such as 2,6-diaminopurine and the reversal of their effects (Miller, 1953), it could be clearly shown that adenine as well as auxin is required for each of the several types of growth tested, including cell elongation. The interaction of adenine with IAA, therefore, can hardly be one of competitive inhibition. Also other naturally occurring purines and pyrimidines may enhance or modify the effect of adenine in bud formation (Skoog, 1954*b*).

Isolation of Kinetin; Kinins

In view of the above, a search was made for possible reaction products or complexes of IAA and adenine within the tobacco tissues. In this connexion it was found that excised pith tissue responds differently to IAA in the absence and presence of vascular tissue; in the former case there is only cell enlargement, whereas in the latter case some cell division and eventually root formation occur as well. The presence of a factor in the vascular tissue which induces division in the pith cells (especially in the presence of added auxin) was demonstrated and was shown to be present also in various natural products (Jablonski & Skoog, 1954). Later a crystalline substance with properties of this type was isolated from commercial DNA preparations, identified as 6-(furfurylamino) purine, and synthesized (Miller *et al.* 1956). The structural formula is given in Text-Fig. 1. Because of its activity in promoting cell division it was named kinetin. More than twenty analogues (all adenine derivatives) have since been found to possess similar activity to varying degrees, but none has been markedly more active than the furfuryladenine (Okumura, von Saltza, Strong, Miller & Skoog, 1955). The following are among the more

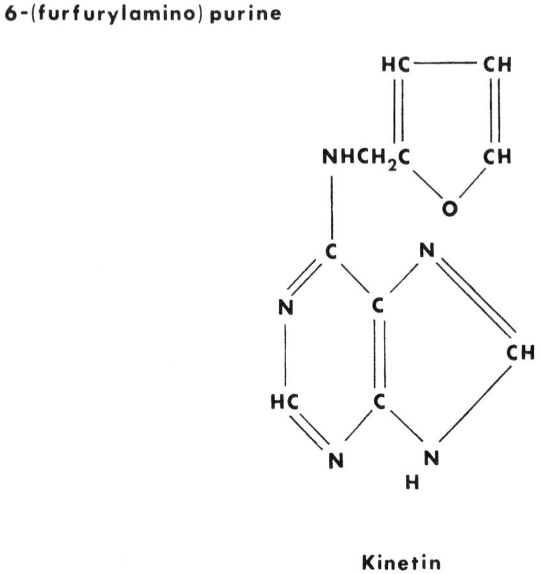

6-(furfurylamino) purine

Kinetin

Text-Fig. 1. Structural formula of kinetin.

active derivatives (active in tobacco callus or pith cultures in concentrations of 1–10 μg./l.): benzyl-, phenyl-, 2-thenyl-, butyl-, amyl-, hexyl-. Of the alkyl derivatives ethyl- and heptyl- were slightly active, but methyl-, octyl- and decyl- were not active in our tests. Substitutions of polar groups in the side chain has led to inactivation. Substitutions in the purine nucleus almost invariably has led to complete loss in activity, but in the case of —NH$_2$ substituted in the 2 position some activity was retained. Further details will be published by Strong *et al.* As mentioned, these substances with physiological activity similar to that of kinetin have been named kinins. This generic term may also include structurally different substances of the type reported by Shantz & Steward (1955*a, b*).

Kinetin-IAA Interactions in Growth of Cells

The requirement for both IAA and kinetin in the growth of excised pith tissue is demonstrated in Pl. 1, fig. 1. The effect on cell division may be seen by comparison of Pl. 1, fig. 2*a* and *b*. Detailed studies of cytological effects of kinetin in tobacco pith have been carried out by Drs Patau and Das in co-operation with the writer. Early stages in the division of cells are shown in Pl. 1, fig. 3, and summaries of counts of mitosis and of newly formed cells plotted as functions of concentration and length of kinetin treatments in the presence of IAA, are shown in Text-Fig. 2*a* and *b* respectively. A diagram (Text-Fig. 3) illustrating the interaction of kinin

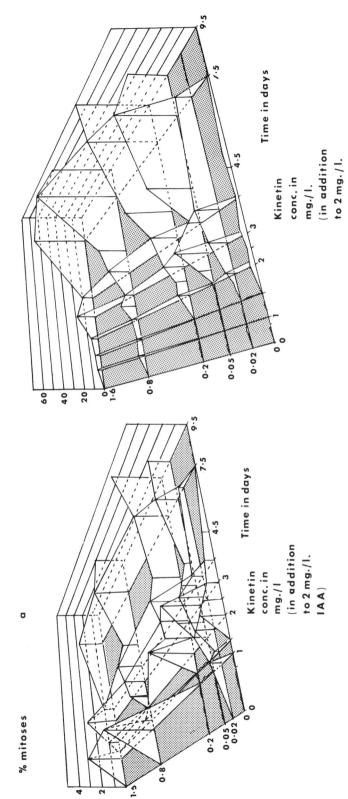

Text-Fig. 2. Effect of kinetin as a function of concentration and time of treatment on: (*a*) the rate of cell division (percentage mitosis), and (*b*) the number of new cells formed in tobacco pith sections cultured on modified White's nutrient agar media with 2·0 mg./l. IAA added (Das, Patau & Skoog, 1956).

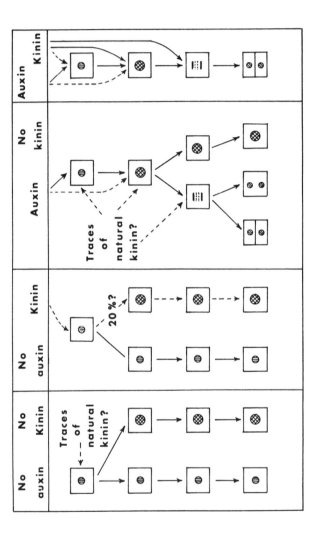

Text-Fig. 3. Diagram representing action of kinetin and IAA, separately and in combination, on DNA synthesis, mitosis and cell division in to-bacco pith tissue (Patau & Das, unpublished).

and auxin (kinetin and IAA) in DNA[*] increase, mitosis and cytokinesis, has been prepared by Dr Patau. It shows that some DNA formation may be induced by kinetin in the absence of added IAA, and vice versa that some mitoses may be induced (Naylor, Sander & Skoog, 1954), and also a few cell divisions may be induced by IAA in the absence of added kinetin, whereas no cell division or mitosis is found in the controls. These slight effects of the treatments with only one substance undoubtedly depend on the presence of small endogenous contents of the other. In general it can be stated that both substances are required for active DNA synthesis, mitosis and cell division to proceed continuously.

Kinetin-IAA Interactions in Organ Formation

Perhaps we may think of these definite and rather quantitative effects of IAA and kinetin on cells as primary manifestations of their growth regulatory action. However this may be, the morphogenetic influences of the substances are numerous and "pliable," that is, subject to modification by a variety of factors and/or conditions. They are, nevertheless, consistently reproducible, and distinct to the visual observer to a degree that can only be poorly reflected in black and white photographs, weights or dimensional measurements of various types.

(a) *Effects of concentration.* A most striking morphogenetic effect of kinetin is in the initiation and development of buds, as observed in tobacco callus or stem-tissue cultures (Pl. 2). This effect is greatly dependent on the concentration and on the presence of other factors, especially the auxin level in the nutrient medium. The influence of a high phosphate level must also be noted. In Pl. 3 is shown the effect of increasing kinetin concentrations on first generation subcultures of stem segments grown on modified White's medium (Miller & Skoog, 1953) with a constant 2 mg./l. level of IAA. Some growth, mainly cell enlargement and the formation of a few short roots, is seen to have occurred in controls. The effect of 0·02 mg./l. is mainly on undifferentiated callus growth, whereas that of 0·5 and 1·0 mg./l. is mainly on bud formation and development with a repression of root formation. Still higher concentrations of kinetin tend to inhibit growth under the conditions of this experiment, but are not very toxic, so that cultures with high kinetin levels actually will remain alive for months longer than the control or low-level kinetin cultures. The interaction of kinetin at two levels (0·2 and 1·0 mg./l.) with increasing concentrations of IAA from 0 to 3·0 mg./l. are compared with each other and with controls in Pl. 4, and the same experiment with the addition of 3 g./l. casein hydrolysate in the medium is represented in Pl. 5. The actual appearance of the cultures in Pls. 4 and 5 receiving 1·0 mg./l. kinetin may be better judged perhaps from the photographs shown in Pl. 6A and B

[*] DNA measured spectrophotometrically on large numbers of individual, Feulgen-stained nuclei.

respectively. Points to be noted are: (1) Very little growth occurred without addition of either kinetin or IAA. (2) In the presence of $0 \cdot 2$–$3 \cdot 0$ mg./l. IAA these callus tissues subcultured from stem segments, as expected, underwent considerable enlargement associated with some cell division and root development from the cambial or phloem derivatives. (3) $0 \cdot 2$ mg./l. kinetin alone permitted sufficient growth to produce a bud or two per piece of tissue. (4) With increasing IAA concentrations growth increased, but bud formation was repressed by the higher IAA levels. (5) $1 \cdot 0$ mg./l. kinetin was more effective than was $0 \cdot 2$ mg./l. in promoting growth, especially bud development, but with increasing IAA concentration growth increased and again bud formation was gradually repressed in favour of callus growth. (6) The apparently greater increase in size of callus with high IAA levels and $0 \cdot 2$ mg./l. as compared with $1 \cdot 0$ mg./l. kinetin is misleading. It reflects "watery" tissues with a large proportion of loosely packed cells as compared with very firm tissues consisting of numerous small "meristematic" cells. (7) Finally, it should be mentioned that both kinetin levels used in this experiment were too high for promotion of root growth (cf. Pl. 3).

(b) *Casein hydrolysate and amino-acid effects on growth.* Stimulatory effects of casein hydrolysate and amino-acid mixtures have been reported in studies of cell division of carrot tissues (see Steward & Shantz, 1954). Recent claims that suitable mixtures of known amino acids will replace the requirement for the coconut factor in cell division (Paris & Duhamet, 1953) seem not to be generally true, but this may be so in specific cases. In the present experiments (Pls. 4, 5 and 6) the effect of casein hydrolysate was a marked general promotion of growth, but only in the presence of added IAA or kinetin. In the presence of high auxin levels the development of roots was favoured; the inhibiting action of IAA on root elongation was counteracted. In the presence of kinetin, especially at the higher ($1 \cdot 0$ mg./l.) level, bud development was enhanced, and again the inhibiting action of IAA was counteracted.

Tests of the influence of individual amino acids have shown that the beneficial role of the casein hydrolysate in promoting bud development in this case can be explained, even if not entirely accounted for, by the effect of tyrosine, as is shown in Pl. 7. Phenylalanine by comparison only had a small effect, and tryptophane, which under these conditions is oxidatively deaminated to give a high level of IAA, as expected, did not promote bud formation. A large number of roots may be seen to be present in the tyrosine-treated tissues. These, however, have arisen from the stems after the buds were formed, and in the early stages only buds were observed. It would seem that the effect of tyrosine was exerted especially on stem and leaf development. However, it appears from the results already presented that no sharp distinction except in a quantitative sense can be made between growth-factor requirements for buds and roots.

The difficulty in the past of obtaining root formation directly in tobacco callus seems to be eliminated by the use of suitable proportions of kinetin and IAA. Still there is evidence of other factors which strongly favour the expression of root formation in these cultures. Nevertheless, it would seem that the two-factor control of lateral root formation explored by Torrey (1950, 1955) and Geissbühler (1953) may be largely a kinin-auxin phenomenon. Although kinetin in minute concentrations favours the development of seedling root systems, in higher amounts it strikingly inhibits elongation and branching of roots and instead promotes growth in thickness of the primary root (Pl. 8, fig. 1). In fact, in a certain kinetin concentration range, the roots formed in tobacco callus cultures may even develop nodules superficially similar to those on legumes (Pl. 8, fig. 2). Similarly in cuttings, low kinetin levels favour and high levels inhibit root formation.

(c) *Variability in the response by different tissues or strains of callus.* In experiments with stem segment cultures (Pl. 9) kinetin, supplied alone tended to retard rather than to promote bud formation in the early stages, although in later stages more buds were found on the kinetin-treated segments than on controls. Furthermore, these buds, in contrast with the control ones, continued to elongate in the absence of root formation.[*] Note, however, the relatively tremendous growth and organ-forming activity induced by combinations of adenine and kinetin. It may be seen that the phenyl derivative which is less active than kinetin, possibly for this very reason, has given a marked boost to growth, including bud formation of the segments, but in combination with adenine it was less effective than kinetin.

Differences in response of tissues derived originally from the same parent stock can be demonstrated also in callus strains derived from the internal phloem, cambium or pith of the stem, but probably are due to differences in capacities acquired in the course of subculturing and without reference to the parent type of tissue. In part they may be merely quantitative in nature. In this connexion, Dr Tryon's work with strains of cultures of Turkish tobacco of common origin is of special interest (Tryon, 1955, 1956). She has developed certain strains which, when subcultured on modified White's medium, grow as undifferentiated masses, others which continuously form buds, and still others which exhibit continuous and profuse root formation. By suitable additions of IAA and kinetin under favourable P and N nutrient conditions she has been able to repress bud formation or root formation respectively. In the case of a "non-differentiating" strain of Wis. no. 38 tobacco she recently has obtained bud formation, by combined treatments with kinetin, adenine and

[*] Thus kinetin in this instance (and especially kinetin plus tyrosine) fills the specifications for the effect if not the properties of a caulocaline (cf. Went, 1951; Skoog, 1954*a*; Howell & Skoog, 1955).

tyrosine, whereas with either of the latter two substances alone no buds were obtained. These results further illustrate the variable and multiple nature of growth-factor requirements for organ formation.

Interactions of kinetin and IAA very comparable to those reported here have also been observed in the growth and differentiation of moss cultures by Eakin & Gorton (private communication, see also Skinner & Shive, 1955). Rather different are the effects of kinetin in promoting germination of lettuce seed and rapid development of hypocotyls and cotyledons in the dark as well as in promoting expansion of leaf disks in the dark (Miller, 1956). The latter effect has also been observed by Liverman et al. (private communication). In these cases, in which the primary effect of kinetin is on cell enlargement rather than cell division, the substance may be said to replace the well-known "morphogenetic" action of light, but its effect is not identical with that of light in all particulars.

III. Discussion and Conclusions

The evidence we have obtained points to a uniformity in growth-factor requirements and regulatory mechanisms for all types of growth. Definite parallelisms in these respects are found in cell elongation and cell division of tissues, in the initiation of roots and buds, and in the subsequent development of these organs. Interactions between IAA and kinetin and between these and other factors appear to exert decisive influences in each case. Both types of chemical seem to be required for growth. Low levels of one with high levels of the other and vice versa lead to opposite morphological end-results. The same holds true in cuttings. For example, bean stems dipped into auxin solution and planted with their basal ends in water or nutrient solution will show increased root formation and decreased lateral bud development as compared with untreated controls. Cuttings dipped in a kinetin solution, on the other hand, will show enhanced bud development and no or markedly retarded development of adventitious roots. Thus, all the evidence reported here points to quantitative interactions rather than qualitative action of growth factors in the regulation of growth. This general conclusion is, of course, directly opposite to concepts of specific organ-forming substances (as advocated by Bouillenne (1950) or Gautheret (1950)). It tends to minimize the significance of slight structural modifications found in plants or in cultured tissues, because these, even when consistently reproducible, often must reflect only slight differences in growth-factor contents. The results obtained also are sharply in conflict with the concept of "determination," i.e. irreversible loss in regenerative capacities of cells and tissues, in ontogeny.

On the other hand, in drawing attention to the complexities and levels of chemical interactions in the regulation of growth, they suggest the futility of attempts to interpret growth phenomena on the basis of very precise computations of the interaction between only two factors in a multifactor system, as in the determinations of so-called auxin-antiauxin competitions (cf. McRae, Foster & Bonner, 1953; Bonner & Foster, 1956). Even though they exist, as experimentally determined, they can have meaning only in a general sense. At the other extreme are schemes postulating interaction of fields or "gradients" which are too general or non-specific to be meaningful, as, for example, Wardlaw's (1955) discussion based on Turing's (1952) proposal. Clearly actual control mechanisms must be too heterogeneous both in detailed structure and in location (dispersion) within the cells and tissues to be amenable to such treatments. In a recent discussion of our work, Thimann (1956) points to certain similarities in the structure of adenine, kinetin and IAA, as well as of biotin. It must be considered, however, that his structural formulae are purposely sketched in a suggestive manner with disregard for exact geometric relationships demanded by atomic considerations. We rather feel that the evidence we now have for the combined action of IAA and adenine or kinetin, or both, in processes varying from nucleic acid synthesis, cell division and cell elongation to the regulation of organ formation, would preclude an interpretation of the action of these substances merely on speculative considerations of competitive interaction between them.

As regards the pertinence of the present results to ontogeny, more work is needed. We do know that both kinins, of as yet unknown chemical nature, and auxins are present in leaf and stem tissues. It may be logically assumed that they participate in meristematic activity, differentiation and organ development in the intact plant in the same manner as in tissue cultures. It would appear, therefore, that the results reported here go a long way towards answering the original question of the dual action of auxin on growth and in inhibition of buds. The exact chemical nature of the interaction of IAA and kinetin remains to be determined, but there can be little doubt that both are involved in nucleic acid metabolism, including nucleic acid synthesis. It is possible to visualize, therefore, an essentially nuclear mechanism of growth regulation which possesses recognized means for interaction with the cytoplasm and which also is considered to be represented rather directly in the synthesis of large molecular structural units of the cell walls.

We are approaching the stage, therefore, where sharp distinctions between stimuli, "energy-furnishing" metabolites and structural units are disappearing, as these can be seen to grade into each other in integrated biosynthetic systems which function in all types of growth, and which would account for the remarkable uniformity of the regulatory mechanisms in the different phases of growth and morphogenesis that we have observed. The present results suggest that numerous potential possibilities exist for the regulation of growth by chemical manipulations of the media at such different levels as 1 μg./l. hormone and 400 mg./l. inorganic

PLATE 1

Fig. 1. Effects of kinetin and IAA on growth of excised tobacco pith tissue cultured on modified White's nutrient agar. Age of cultures 49 days.

Fig. 2. Sections through pith tissue cultured on modified White's nutrient agar. *a*, control. *b*, with $0 \cdot 2$ mg./l. kinetin and 2 mg./l. IAA added to medium.

Fig. 3. Early stage of cell division in tobacco pith tissue cultured on modified White's nutrient agar with $0 \cdot 2$ mg./l. kinetin and $2 \cdot 0$ mg./l. IAA added. Age of culture, 10 days. Section stained with Harris's haematoxylin showing metaphase, presumably leading to first division, in large cell, and divided adjacent cells (Das, Patau & Skoog, 1956).

PLATE 2

Bud formation in tobacco callus. Callus (fifth subculture of tobacco stem) on modified White's medium. A, with kinetin $0 \cdot 2$ mg./l.; B, with kinetin $0 \cdot 2$ mg./l. plus IAA 2 mg./l.; C, with kinetin $0 \cdot 2$ mg./l., IAA 2 mg./l. and in addition KH_2PO_4 400 mg./l. Age of cultures, *c*. 45 days.

PLATE 3

Effect of kinetin concentration (in 0–10 mg./l. range) on growth and organ formation of tobacco callus cultured on modified White's nutrient agar with $2 \cdot 0$ mg./l. IAA added. Age of cultures, 44 days. (Skoog *et al.*)

PLATES 4 AND 5

Effect of increasing IAA concentration at different kinetin levels on the growth and organ formation of tobacco callus cultured on modified White's nutrient agar; (Plate 4) without, and (Plate 5) with, 3 g./l. casein hydrolysate added. Age of cultures, 62 days (Skoog *et al.*).

PLATE 6

A and B. Representative flasks from treatments with $1 \cdot 0$ mg./l. kinetin, in lower rows of Pls. 4 and 5 respectively (Skoog *et al.*).

PLATE 7

Effect of individual amino-acids on the growth and organ formation in tobacco callus cultured on modified White's nutrient medium with 2 mg./l. IAA, $0 \cdot 2$ mg./l. kinetin and additions. K, none; KPh, DL-phenylalanine 150 mg./l.; KTy, DL-tyrosine 210 mg./l.; and KTr, DL-tryptophan 60 mg./l. Age of cultures 84 days.

PLATE 8

Fig. 1. Effect of kinetin concentration on lateral root development in seedling root of bean.

Fig. 2. Nodule-like proliferations appearing in place of lateral rootlets on a tobacco root system formed on callus culture *in vitro*. Sample from control culture to left. Samples from low kinetin treatments to right.

PLATE 9

Effect of adenine and kinetin or 6-(phenylamino) purine (phenyladenine) singly and in combination on growth and bud formation in tobacco stem segments. Stem segments cultured on modified White's medium with additions. O, none; A, adenine 54 mg./l.; K, kinetin $0 \cdot 86$ mg./l.; AK, A + K; P, 6-(phenylamino) purine $0 \cdot 8$ mg./l.; AP, A + P. Age of cultures, 38 days. (All treatments with K or P are 4×10^{-6}M and with adenine 4×10^{-4}M.)

PLATE I

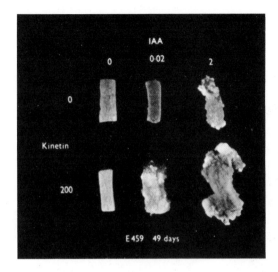

Fig. 1

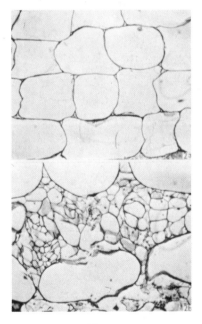

Fig. 2

Fig. 3

PLATE 2

PLATE 3

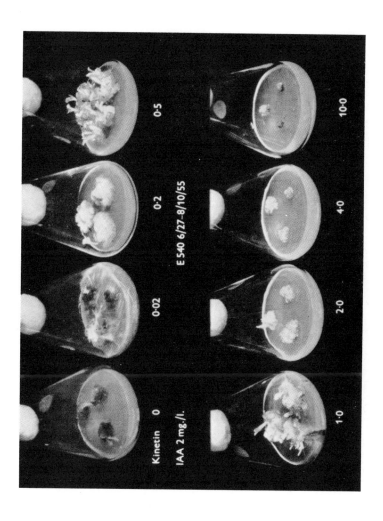

PLATE 4

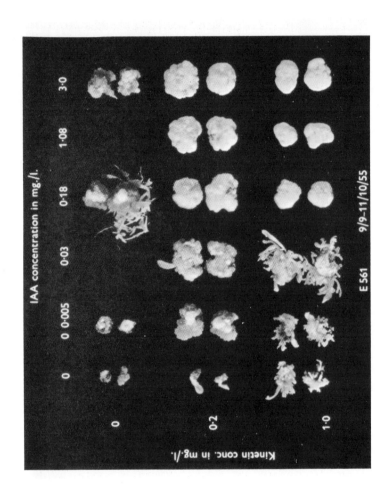

PLATE 5

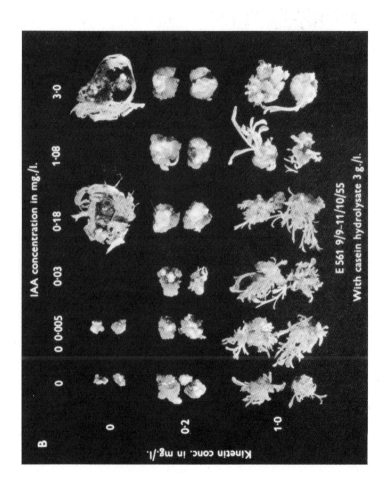

PLATE 6

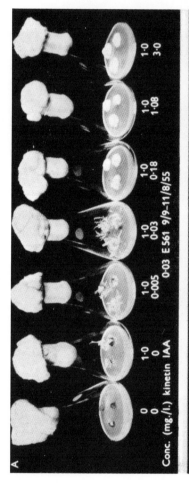

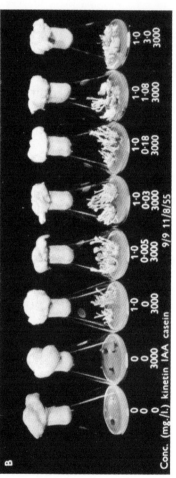

PLATE 7

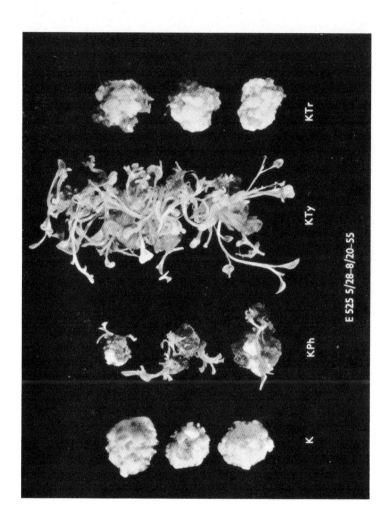

PLATE 8

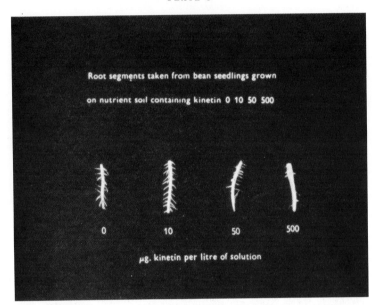

Root segments taken from bean seedlings grown
on nutrient soil containing kinetin 0 10 50 500

0   10   50   500

μg. kinetin per litre of solution

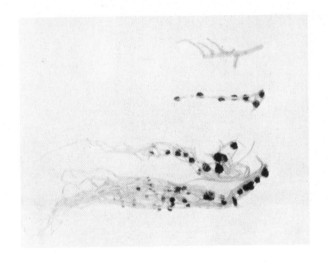

PLATE 9

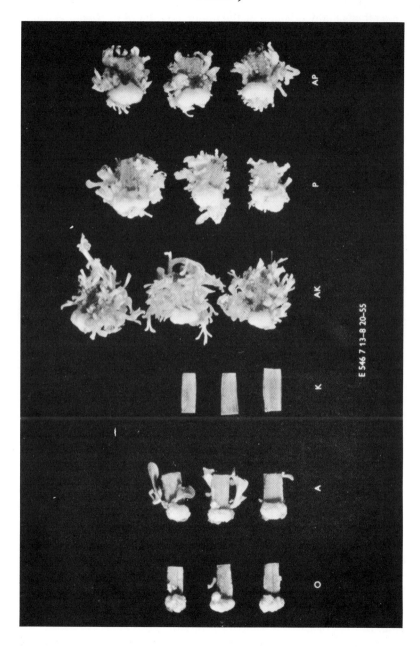

phosphate. The reason for this must be that cellular constituents of all types, including growth factors, are so closely interlocked that a change in one affects many others. For the understanding of the detailed function or biological action of any one growth substance, therefore, we must also learn a great deal about many others.

References

Bonner, J. & Foster, R. J. (1956). In *The Chemistry and Mode of Action of Plant Growth Substances*, p. 295. Ed. Wain, R. L. and Weightman, F. London: Butterworth's Scientific Publications.
Bouillenne, A. (1950). *Année biol.* **54**, 597.
Das, N. K., Patau, K. & Skoog, F. (1956). *Physiol. Plant.* **9**, 640.
Gautheret, R. J. (1950). *Année biol.* **54**, 719.
Gautheret, R. J. (1955). *Ann. Rev. Pl. Physiol.* **6**, 433.
Geissbühler, H. (1953). *Ber. schweiz. bot. Ges.* **63**, 27.
Haberlandt, G. (1921). *Beitr. allg. Bot.* **2**, 1.
Howell, R. W. & Skoog, F. (1955). *Amer. J. Bot.* **42**, 356.
Jablonski, J. R. & Skoog, F. (1954). *Physiol. Plant.* **7**, 16.
McRae, D. H., Foster, R. J. & Bonner, J. (1953). *Plant Physiol.* **28**, 343.
Miller, C. O. (1953). *Proc. Soc. Exp. Biol., N.Y.*, **83**, 561.
Miller, C. O. (1956). *Plant Physiol.* **31**, 318.
Miller, C. O. & Skoog, F. (1953). *Amer. J. Bot.* **40**, 768.
Miller, C. O., Skoog, F., Okumura, F. S., von Saltza, M. H. & Strong, F. M. (1956). *J. Amer. Chem. Soc.* **78**, 1375.
Naylor, J., Sander, G. & Skoog, F. (1954). *Physiol. Plant.* **7**, 25.
Okumura, F. S., von Saltza, M. H., Strong, F. M., Miller, C. O. & Skoog, F. (1955). 28th Meeting Amer. Chem. Soc. Minneapolis, Minn.
Paris, D. & Duhamet, L. (1953). *C.R. Acad. Sci., Paris*, **236**, 1690.
Shantz, E. M. & Steward, F. C. (1955*a*). *J. Amer. Chem. Soc.* **77**, 6351.
Shantz, E. M. & Steward, F. C. (1955*b*). *Pl. Physiol.* Suppl. **30**, 35.
Skinner, C. G. & Shive, W. (1955). *J. Amer. Chem. Soc.* **77**, 6692.
Skoog, F. (1954*a*). In *Dynamics of Growth Processes*, p. 148. Ed. Boell, E. G. Princeton, N.J.: Princeton University Press.
Skoog, F. (1954*b*). In *Abnormal and Pathological Growth*, Brookhaven Symposia in Biol., **6** (BNL 258 (c–19)).
Skoog, F. & Tsui, C. (1948). *Amer. J. Bot.* **35**, 782.
Skoog, F. & Tsui, C. (1951). In *Plant Growth Substances*, p. 263. Madison: University of Wisconsin Press.
Snow, R. (1935). *New Phytol.* **34**, 347.
Steward, F. C. & Shantz, E. M. (1954). *Année biol.* **30**, 139.
Thimann, K. V. (1956). *Amer. Nat.* **40**, 145.
Torrey, J. G. (1950). *Amer. J. Bot.* **37**, 257.
Torrey, J. G. (1956). *Ann. Rev. Pl. Physiol.* **7**, 237.
Tryon, K. (1955). *Amer. J. Bot.* **42**, 604.
Tryon, K. (1956). *Science*, **123**, 590.
Turing, A. M. (1952). *Proc. Roy. Soc. B*, **237**, 37.
Wardlaw, C. W. (1955). *Embryogenesis in Plants*. London: Methuen and Co. Ltd.
Went, F. W. (1951). In *Plant Growth Substances*, p. 287. Ed. Skoog, F. Madison: University of Wisconsin Press.

Effect of Kinetin on Protein Content and
Survival of Detached Xanthium Leaves

Amos E. Richmond
Anton Lang

When a leaf is detached from a plant, its protein content undergoes a prompt and rapid decline [1], the chlorophyll content decreases in close proportion [2], and the life-span of the leaf is markedly reduced. Detached leaves are capable of incorporating labeled nitrogen and carbon into their protein [3, 4]. Thus, their ability to synthesize protein is not altogether lost. However, they seem to have largely lost the ability to synthesize certain amino acids [4], and the ratio between protein synthesis and breakdown is greatly shifted in favor of the latter. Although this characteristic pattern of protein metabolism in detached leaves has led to extensive experimentation, attempts to modify it experimentally have not been successful.

In an attempt to control experimentally the survival and protein balance in detached leaves, we studied the effect of some plant regulators on these processes. Auxin (indole-3-acetic acid) sometimes reduced protein loss, but the effect was slight and erratic. Kinetin [5], in contrast, reduced protein loss in a consistent and striking manner.

The opposite primary leaves of young, vegetative *Xanthium pennsylvanicum* (cocklebur) plants were used in all experiments. Leaves that had reached full expansion or were quite close to reaching it were cut off and inserted with the petioles either into aqueous solutions of kinetin or into water. They were kept in bright, diffuse daylight and in a nearly water-saturated atmosphere (in glass-covered enamel trays) at a temperature of 22° to 25°C. The cuts were renewed every other day; the solutions, every fifth day.

Figure 1 shows the condition of the leaves at the end of an experiment. The leaves that were kept on water lost most of their chlorophyll, but those supplied with kinetin retained their green color.

Figure 2 shows the protein nitrogen and total nitrogen content of the leaf blades after an experimental period of 12 days. The blades of the controls lost 60 percent of their initial protein content. In the blades of leaves that were kept on 5 mg of kinetin per liter, the loss amounted to only 15 percent and was of the same magnitude as it is in attached leaves of comparable age. Leaves kept on 1 mg of kinetin per liter lost 50 per-

Reprinted by permission of the authors and publisher from *Science, 125:* 650–651, 1957. This work was supported in part by research grants from the National Institutes of Health, U.S. Public Health Service (RG-3939), and the University of California Cancer Research Coordinating Committee (Grant Nr. 407).

Fig. 1. Condition of detached *Xanthium* leaves after 10 days'
culture on (from top to bottom) water, 1 mg of kinetin per
liter, and 5 mg of kinetin per liter.

cent of their protein. As has been found before [1], the protein nitrogen
lost by the blades appears as soluble nitrogen in the petioles and the
major veins. The amount of soluble nitrogen (measured as difference between total nitrogen and protein nitrogen) in the blades was about the
same in controls and treated leaves.

The effect of kinetin on condition and protein content of detached
Xanthium leaves has so far been somewhat variable. In one experiment,
the treated leaves were still fully green after a period of 20 days, while
the controls were completely yellow and were dying at the tip and
margins. In other experiments, the difference in the survival period was
smaller. This variability, which seems to depend on the age of the leaves
and on the growing conditions of the plant, should have further investigation. However, there is no doubt that kinetin is capable of reducing or
preventing the accelerated protein loss that is typical of detached leaves;
at the same time, it delays the loss of chlorophyll and extends the life-
span of the leaf. The former effect is very likely the immediate cause of
the two latter.

Kinetin was discovered as a regulator of cell division [5, 6]. However,
several authors [7] found that kinetin promotes the growth of leaf discs,
and this effect was based solely on cell enlargement. In the blade of

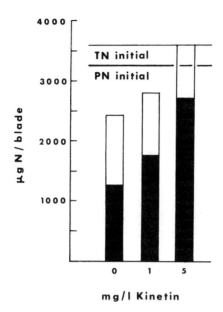

Fig. 2. Protein nitrogen (PN) and total nitrogen (TN) in detached *Xanthium* leaves (blades) after 12 days' culture on water and kinetin solutions. The total columns represent total nitrogen; the solid parts of columns represent protein nitrogen; and the horizontal lines show levels at the start of the experiment.

kinetin-treated, detached *Xanthium* leaves, new cell division cannot be observed either. Cell-division activity thus does not seem to be a premise for the effects of kinetin on the growth of leaf tissue and on its protein metabolism. Whether the last-named effect is an essential feature of the action mechanism of kinetin in growth responses will have to be decided in future work.

References

1. A. C. Chibnall, *Protein Metabolism in Plants* (Yale Univ. Press, New Haven, Conn., 1939), chap. 8; J. Bonner, *Plant Biochemistry* (Academic, New York, 1950), chap. 20.
2. G. Michael, Z. *Botan.* **29**, 385 (1935).
3. A. C. Chibnall and G. H. Wiltshire, *New Phytologist* **53**, 38 (1954).
4. D. W. Racusen and S. Aronoff, *Arch. Biochem. and Biophys.* **51**, 38 (1954).
5. C. O. Miller *et al., J. Am. Chem. Soc.* **78**, 1375 (1956).
6. N. K. Das, K. Patau, F. Skoog, *Physiol. Plantarum* **9**, 640 (1956).
7. C. O. Miller, *Plant Physiol.* **31**, 318 (1956); S. Kuraishi and F. S. Okumura, *Botan. Mag. (Tokyo)* **69**, 300 (1956).

Kinetin-Induced Directed Transport of Substances in Excised Leaves in the Dark

K. Mothes
L. Engelbrecht

If kinetin (6-aminofurfurylpurine) is sprayed on a limited area of an excised mature leaf, numerous substances in the untreated parts will migrate to this "kinetin-locus." This phenomenon can be impressively demonstrated with radioactively labelled amino acids which are applied through the petiole or to the surface of the leaf [1–3].

This directed migration is caused by an accumulation of substances in the kinetin treated tissue. This accumulation corresponds, at least in its last phase, to an active transport and consequently is an energy-requiring process. Kinetin can also inhibit the outward migration of substances [3, 4], and the treated area, therefore, also represents a locus of predominant synthesis. Accumulation, however, is not the consequence of synthesis, but mass-synthesis of protein, for example, is the consequence of an accumulation of amino acids. This has been proved by the finding that those amino acids which cannot be incorporated into protein, such as α-aminoisobutyric acid, are subjected to the kinetin-directed transport and accumulation [5].

Kinetin-treated tissue behaves physiologically like young tissue: it accumulates certain substances and arrests others [3, 6]. Thus kinetin has been found to be a model-substance of the regulative principle which is of decisive importance for the distribution and exchange of substances within the plant. This finding gives us the possibility to induce and influence certain regulations ourselves [3]. Unpublished experiments (with K. Conrad) have shown that indoleacetic acid is also subjected to this directed transport under the influence of kinetin. The frequently observed polarity of substance transport thus can be augmented, eliminated, or reversed by kinetin.

Our previously published experiments were carried out almost exclusively with green leaves in a weak light. Leaves that have been kept in the dark for a considerable time, or are chlorophyll-deficient show the above mentioned effects either only indistinctly or not at all. This may be due to various causes. One might consider that accumulation preferentially takes place in tissue containing functioning chloroplasts exposed to light. But it may also be possible that a good source of ATP is necessary for the energy-requiring processes of accumulation. Such a source might be represented by photophosphorylation. The following experiments demon-

Reprinted by permission of the authors and Pergamon Press Ltd. from *Phytochemistry*, 1: 58–62, 1961.

strate that directed transport and accumulation are also possible in leaves kept in the dark.

Excised leaves of *Nicotiana rustica* were first treated with kinetin, and four days later with glycine-1-^{14}C as shown in Fig. 1. After uptake of the amino acid was complete, half the leaves were kept in the dark and the other half exposed to continuous light, and sampled after varying time periods (Table 1). Radioautographs were taken of one leaf from each group (Fig. 2), and samples of kinetin-treated area from corresponding leaves taken for analysis. The samples were extracted with 80 per cent ethanol, and the extracts examined for radioactivity (Table 3) and chromatographed (Figs. 3 and 4). The insoluble residue was hydrolysed and the activity of the hydrolysate determined.

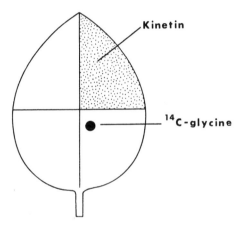

Fig. 1. Scheme showing the local application of kinetin and glycine-(1-^{14}C) to isolated leaves of *Nicotiana rustica*.

TABLE 1

Distribution of Radioactivity at the Kinetin-Locus After Application of Glycine-(1^{14}-C) to Another Site

| Experiment No. | Condition | Duration (hr) | Counts/Min | | | Ratio Sol. Fract./ Insol. Fract. |
			Sol. fract.	Insol. fract.	Total	
1 (a)	light	8½	1443	459	1902	3·2
(b)	dark		1426	437	1863	3·3
2 (a)	light	23	5824	2050	7874	2·9
(b)	dark		3068	784	3852	3·9
3 (a)	light	55	2523	1714	4237	1·5
(b)	dark		2273	816	3088	2·8

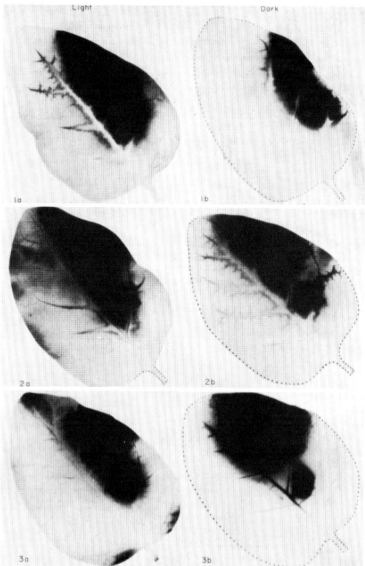

Fig. 2. Radioautographs of leaves of *Nicotiana rustica*. Application of kinetin and glycine-(1-¹⁴C) according to Fig. 1. 1,2,3: the experiment stopped 8½, 23 and 55 hr after the application of glycine, with leaves (*a*) in the light, and (*b*) in the dark.

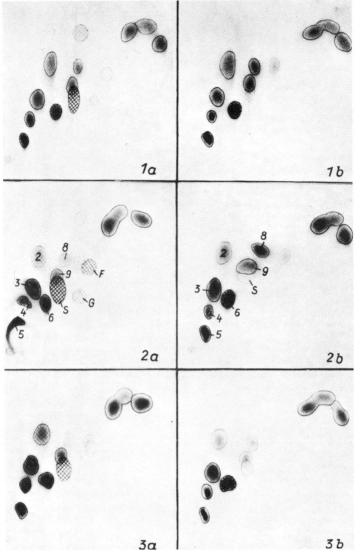

Fig. 3. Chromatograms of soluble fractions (as in Fig. 2)
sprayed with ninhydrin. Radioactive areas are cross-hatched.
Marking of spots: 2 = glutamine, 3 = asparagine, 4 = glutamic
acid, 5 = aspartic acid, 6 = glycine-serine, 8 = alanine, 9 =
threonine, S = sucrose, G = glucose, F = fructose.

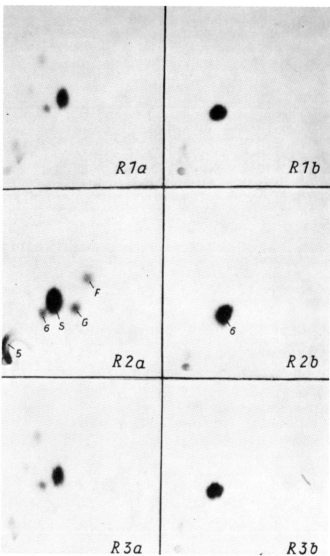

Fig. 4. Radioautographs of the chromatograms of Fig. 3.
Marking of the spots as in Fig. 3.

Results

Before discussing the results in detail some observations must be made
on the metabolic fate of glycine in leaves. Various publications from our
laboratory have demonstrated the rapid transformation of glycine in plants
[6–8]. This process gives rise to CO_2 and an active 1-C-fragment which

by means of folic acid can be used directly, or via methionine or betaine, for methylation and elongation of carbon chains. For example this is the way that the second molecule of glycine is used for the synthesis of serine.

$$CH_2NH_2COOH \longrightarrow (1\text{-}C) + CO_2$$
$$\text{glycine}$$
$$(1\text{-}C) + CH_2NH_2COOH \longrightarrow CH_2OHCHNH_2COOH$$
$$\text{serine}$$

Thus we find large amounts of serine in plant tissues treated with glycine and since glycine can also readily be formed from serine, we find glycine if the tissue is treated with serine. The CO_2 split off from glycine can be used for carboxylation, and photosynthetic assimilation, and thus rapidly appears in certain organic acids and carbohydrates. It can also be eliminated in the normal manner.

Radioautographs of whole leaves (Fig. 2) show that both in the light and in the dark there is a predominant translocation of radioactivity from the site of application to the kinetin-locus. The activity also spreads through the veins to a certain degree. In the leaves exposed to the light considerable radioactivity also appears in the intervenal regions of the left blade. This latter effect seems to be the consequence of CO_2-assimilation by photosynthesis, since the radioactive CO_2 can readily reach the whole leaf.

The distribution of radioactivity in the soluble and insoluble fractions of the kinetin-treated tissues is shown in Table 1. These results confirm the radioautographs. Activity very rapidly migrates into the kinetin-tissue. After 8½ hr there is not much difference in total radioactivity between the leaf exposed to the light and the one in the dark. Also the ratio of the distribution of activity in the soluble, and hydrolysed insoluble fractions is almost the same in the two leaves. In both cases there is much more activity in the soluble fraction than in the insoluble.

After 23 hr the migration of activity into the kinetin tissue has much increased. The leaf exposed to the light now has a much higher activity due to an increase of both soluble and insoluble radioactive compounds, the latter increasing more rapidly. In this leaf the ratio of radioactivity of the soluble to insoluble fraction has decreased (from $3 \cdot 2$ to $2 \cdot 9$), indicating that incorporation of soluble substances into insoluble ones, has increased. In the leaf kept in the dark, on the other hand, the quotient has increased (from $3 \cdot 3$ to $3 \cdot 9$); in this case therefore the inflow of soluble substances exceeds their further assimilation.

After 55 hr the total activity has decreased. Presumably most activity is lost by disappearance of CO_2, even in the light where the CO_2 can easily be reincorporated.

The radioautographs (Fig. 4) of the paper chromatograms (Fig. 3) of the soluble fraction show that in the darkened leaf (1b, 2b, 3b) most of the radioactivity is fixed as glycine and serine. There is, however, always a little activity in monosaccharides and in sucrose; obviously some of the free radioactive CO_2 is transformed by dark assimilation to carbohydrates. Because of the high specific activity of the two amino acids glycine and serine (spot 6, Fig. 4) it is probable that the activity in the dark leaf migrates primarily in the form in which it was applied, that is as glycine and its rapidly appearing metabolic product serine.

The radioautographs of the leaves exposed to light (1a, 2a, 3a of Fig. 4) show remarkably less activity in the glycine-serine spot, but very high activity in the products of decarboxylation and CO_2 assimilation, sucrose, glucose and fructose, as well as in several amino acids.

The remarkable difference between leaves in the light and leaves in the dark might indicate that metabolism of the glycine and serine is increased by light. But this problem needs further investigation. It is possible, for example, that in the light glycine is partly transformed at the site of application and that the transformation products, such as carbohydrates, migrate to the kinetin-locus.

The chemical nature of the insoluble compounds formed from glycine will be reported in another publication (Parthier and Wollgiehn).

Discussion

It has been shown that protein-forming amino acids can be accumulated by kinetin-treated tissue in the dark. This might be of great importance for a closer understanding of the way in which concentrations increase in those organs deficient in chloroplasts, or which are growing in the dark: e.g. the phloem, storage organs, fructified ovula, root tips and in young organs etc.

It is not clear, whether the great difference in the total activity of the kinetin tissue between leaves in the light and in the dark (Table 1, experiments 2a and 2b) is due to an extraordinarily high loss of activity in the form of CO_2 in the darkened leaf, whereas in the light the bulk of this CO_2 can immediately be reassimilated. It is, however, more probable that kinetin-induced directed transport is greatly promoted by light. In leaves which have starved for a longer time than those used in these experiments the directed transport to the kinetin-locus takes place either poorly or not at all. Apparently there is a factor, other than kinetin, necessary to make migration possible. We are inclined to suggest that ATP is this factor.

Since kinetin has a promoting effect on the accumulation of substances with very different chemical constitutions, it seems unlikely to function as a carrier itself; it may, however, contribute to the formation of or regeneration of a natural carrier system. Without having concrete proof as yet in favour of any definite concept, most authors [9, 10] incline to a hypothesis which may be expressed in the following scheme:

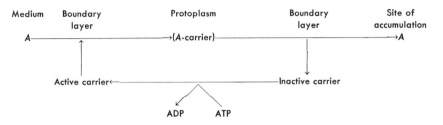

At the boundary layer an amino acid A is transformed to a compound "A-carrier" with the help of a specific substance which has been activated in some way by ATP. This "A-carrier" dissociates at the boundary of the accumulating system (vacuole membrane, mitochondrial membrane, or plastid membrane) releasing the amino acid and regenerating, not the carrier substance itself, but an energy-poor form of it which is therefore inactive. This form is transformed back to the active carrier by the participation of ATP. The ADP resulting must be regenerated by respiration or photophosphorylation to form ATP. In chlorophyll-deficient or starving leaves it is presumed that the ATP regenerating system is not sufficiently active to carry out the cycle.

Besides the unspecific factors, ATP and kinetin, accumulation would also need specific ones, the carriers. Experiments with animal cells, however, make it improbable that every substance has a specific carrier; rather there exists something like enzyme-group-specificity [9, 10]. Perhaps the peculiar differences of translocation direction described by Nelson and Garham [11] are due to such group-specific carriers. We also are inclined to interpret the accelerated efflux of protein degradation products in the presence of asparagine as determined by the more rapid yellowing of the leaves [12] with a blocking of group-specific carriers which are thus rendered incapable of binding other amino acids that are required for protein synthesis.

Experimental

Plants of *Nicotiana rustica* were cultivated in the greenhouse in daylight supplemented with fluorescent light. At the start of the experiment (4 March) the second full-grown leaf (counted from the tip) was excised from a number of plants. The leaves were kept in the laboratory in a humid chamber with moderate diffuse daylight (2 m from a south window) and their right upper quarter was sprayed twice with kinetin (30 mg/l.) (Fig. 1). Four days later, when the untreated parts of the leaves were already distinctly lighter than the kinetin area, 7 μl. of a

$0 \cdot 01$ M glycine-1-^{14}C solution ($0 \cdot 7$ μC) were applied to a small area about 1 cm below the kinetin-treated quarter, avoiding the larger veins. Since weak light increases the rate of uptake, all the leaves were exposed to a moderate light during this period. After the complete uptake of the solution (1 to 2 hr) half of the leaves were put into total darkness, and the other half into continuous light of fluorescent lamps of about 1000 lx. The leaves were sampled after 8½ hr (1a and b), 23 hr (2a and b) and 55 hr (3a and b). One leaf of each group was oven-dried and radioautographed (Fig. 2), and 450 mg of fresh material from the kinetin-treated area of another leaf was extracted with 80 per cent ethanol. The residue was hydrolysed with 6 N HCl for 14 hr at 100°. The total hydrolysis mixture was evaporated to dryness on a steam bath, and made up to 1 ml with H_2O. The radioactivity of both the soluble fraction and of the hydrolysed ethanol insoluble fraction was determined under comparable conditions with a Geiger-Müller tube in an infinitely thin layer (Table 1). 50 μl. of each of the fractions were chromatographed two dimensionally on Schleicher and Schüll paper 2043b. The chromatograms of the soluble fractions are shown in Fig. 3. The same chromatograms were radioautographed with Diavidox X-rayfilm (Fig. 4).

References

1. Mothes, K., and L. Engelbrecht, *Monatsber. Dtsch. Akad. Wiss.*, 1: 367, 1959.

2. Mothes, K., L. Engelbrecht, and O. Kulajewa, *Flora, Jena, 147:* 445, 1959.

3. Mothes, K., *Naturwissenschaften, 47:* 337, 1960.

4. Engelbrecht, L., and K. Mothes, *Plant Cell Physiol.*, 1961.

5. Mothes, K., L. Engelbrecht, and H. R. Schütte, *Physiol. Plant., 14:* 72, 1961.

6. Engelbrecht, L., *Flora, Jena, 150:* 73, 1961.

7. Reinbothe, H., *Flora, Jena, 150:* 128, 1961.

8. Reinbothe, H., and K. Mothes, *Tetrahedron Letters, 25:* 32, 1960.

9. Heinz, E., *J. Biol. Chem., 211:* 781, 1954.

10. Heinz, E., and P. M. Walsh, *J. Biol. Chem., 233:* 1488, 1958.

11. Nelson, C. D., and P. R. Garham, *Can. J. Bot., 37:* 431, 1959.

12. Michael, G., *Z. Bot., 29:* 385, 1935.

Incorporation of a Kinin, N,6-Benzyladenine into Soluble RNA

J. Eugene Fox

The broad spectrum of biological activity exhibited by kinetin (6-furfurylaminopurine) and its analogues raises the possibility that certain 6-substituted purines have an important role in the control of growth and development of higher plants. The fact that many plant tissues require a kinin for in vitro growth [15], that kinins can exhibit profound growth stimulating effects in concentrations as low as 0.004 mg per liter [17], and that natural kinins have been partially purified from several plant sources lend support to this hypothesis.

Despite the potential significance of this group of plant growth regulators, only a single published study exists concerning the metabolic fate of a kinin in plant tissues. McCalla, Morré, and Osborne [14] in 1962 demonstrated that senescing cocklebur and bean leaves converted N,6-benzyladenine-8-C^{14} into a number of low molecular weight substances which included adenylic, guanylic, and inosinic acids, benzyladenosine, and probably benzyladenylic acid. In addition they reported that although there seemed to be a tiny amount of a labeled compound in alkaline hydrolysates of cocklebur leaf RNA which was chromatographically similar to benzyladenylic acid, the amount was too small for confirmation, and it was concluded that benzyladenine is not incorporated into RNA to any significant extent.

If, however, one desires information dealing with the role of kinins in cell division and growth, it would seem appropriate to investigate a system in which kinins are limiting for these processes. Accordingly tobacco and soybean tissue cultures which have an absolute kinin requirement for in vitro proliferation were chosen for this study; evidence is presented here that a kinin, N,6-benzyladenine (BA)* is incorporated into the soluble RNA of these cultures. A preliminary report of these findings has been made [9].

Materials and Methods

Synthesis of C^{14} Labeled N,6-Benzyladenine

The general synthetic method is essentially that of Daly and Christensen [6] in which 6-chloropurine is refluxed with the appropriate amine. In the present study, however, the reaction was carried out in water instead

* Abbreviations: BA, N,6-benzyladenine; t-RNA, transfer RNA; m-RNA, messenger RNA.

Reprinted by permission of the publisher from *Plant Physiology*, 41: 75–82, 1966. This work was supported by National Science Foundation Grants G21765 and GB3132.

of n-butanol because of the relative insolubility of the end product compared to the reactants and possible impurities and the consequent ease of purification.

The synthesis of N,6-benzyladenine-8-C^{14} (BA-8-C^{14}) was achieved by refluxing 2.15 mg of 6-chloropurine-8-C^{14} (Calbiochem, specific activity 3.6 mc/mm) for 8 hours in 50 ml water containing a like amount of unlabeled 6-chloropurine and 1.0 ml benzylamine. The reaction mixture was taken to dryness in a rotary evaporator, the crystalline material washed twice with 2.0 ml of ice cold water, and the residue taken up in 10 ml hot 95% ethanol. This preparation was further purified by chromatography on acid washed Whatman No. 1 paper.

Preliminary studies with unlabeled material indicated that such a procedure resulted in better than 80% yields of pure white, crystalline material, mp 231 to 232°, presumed to be N,6-benzyladenine and having ultraviolet spectra (determined with a Bausch and Lomb model 505 recording spectrophotometer) as follows: λ max 0.1 n NH_4OH 275 mμ, λ max 0.1 n HCl 274.5 mμ, λ max H_2O pH 6.0 269.5 mμ. The melting point and ultraviolet spectra are in good agreement with published values for N,6-benzyladenine [2]. In addition this material proved to have excellent kinin activity in both tobacco and soybean test systems, inducing detectable proliferation in the latter at concentrations as low as 0.1 μg/liter.

Benzyl labeled N,6-benzyladenine (BA-benzyl-C^{14}) was synthesized in a similar manner by reacting 14.92 μm of benzylamine-7-C^{14} (Volk, specific activity 6.7 mc/mm) with 16.18 μm (2.5 mg) 6-chloropurine. For the preparation of some batches, benzylamine-7-C^{14} · HCl (Calbiochem, specific activity 4.1 mc/mm) was used.

Preparation of Tissue Extracts

The origin of the soybean and tobacco tissue cultures used here, their absolute dependence upon a kinin for in vitro cultivation, and their growth on various levels of kinin and auxin have previously been described [8, 10].

For the preparation of nucleotides for anion exchange chromatography, tissues were ground in a Waring blendor with sufficient boiling 95% ethanol to achieve a final concentration of 70% ethanol. The extract was centrifuged at $3000 \times g$ for 20 minutes, the clear supernatant fluid decanted, and the pellet reextracted with successive washes of hot 95% ethanol, absolute acetone, acetone-diethyl ether 1:1, v/v, and 70% ethanol. A final hot 95% ethanol wash was essentially free of detectable C^{14}. The pellet was then stirred into 10 times its volume of 1 n KOH and incubated at 28° for 18 hours. Potassium was removed as the perchlorate by centrifuging at pH 7.5. DNA polynucleotides were then precipitated at pH 3.5 (HCl) in the presence of magnesium ions by adding 3 volumes of ice-cold 95% ethanol and allowing the whole to stand at 0° for 6 hours. Precipitated material was centrifuged off, washed twice with cold 70% ethanol, and taken up in a small volume of water adjusted to pH 8.0 with NaOH. The supernatant fraction, containing RNA nucleotides, as well as the ethanol, acetone and ether extracts were taken to small volumes in a rotary evaporator.

RNA nucleotides were fractionated on Dowex-1 anion exchange resin by a method differing only in minor respects from that of Cohn and Volkin [4], and described in the legend to Fig. 2.

In other experiments tissues were homogenized at 2° in 0.2 м Tris-HCl buffer, pH 7.6, containing 0.5 м sucrose. The homogenate was centrifuged in a Spinco Model L ultracentrifuge at 12,000 × g for 15 minutes. The sediment was discarded and the supernatants centrifuged at 105,000 × g for 180 minutes. The particulate fraction thus obtained was washed by resuspension in the homogenizing medium and a second sedimentation. The centrifugate (assumed to contain ribosomal RNA) and the supernatant fraction (soluble RNA) were treated by the method of Bergquist and Matthews [1] which involves extensive dialysis and reprecipitation of the RNA and which is designed to minimize contamination of RNA by low molecular weight, nonpolynucleotide materials.

Total nucleic acids were extracted for methylated albumin chromatography by a method essentially that described by Cherry [3]. Preparation of the methylated albumin and fractionation of nucleic acids on columns of this material followed the procedures of Mandell and Hershey [13].

Estimation of Radioactivity

Distribution of radioactivity on paper chromatograms was determined either by autoradiography on Kodak no-screen x-ray film or by scanning with a Nuclear-Chicago Actigraph II paper strip counter. For an estimation of the amount of radioactivity on chromatograms, strips of paper approximately 1.5 × 3 cm were immersed in 15 ml of a solution for scintillation counting [50 mg of 1,4-bis-2-(4-methyl-5-phenyloxazolyl) benzene and 3 g of p-terphenyl per liter of toluene] in standard counting vials. Samples were assayed for radioactivity in a Packard tri-carb model 334 liquid scintillation spectrometer.

Fractions from anion exchange or methylated albumin chromatography were dried in a stream of air at 60° onto Whatman No. 1 paper strips which were counted by liquid scintillation. Alternatively in some experiments fractions were pooled, taken to dryness, made up to a small volume in water and counted in duplicate or triplicate by liquid scintillation spectrometry (50 μl portions of the sample were added to a counting vial which contained 5 ml absolute ethanol and 10 ml of the counting solution previously described).

Results

Metabolism of N,6-Benzyladenine-8-C^{14}

About 41% of the C^{14} supplied in the medium as BA-8-C^{14} (1.0–2.0 mg/liter) was recovered by extraction from tobacco tissue harvested after 35 days culture (avg yield: 31 mg tissue per ml medium). No attempts were made to recover possible excretion products in the medium or the atmosphere or residual radioactivity in the material insoluble after alkaline hydrolysis. From soybeans grown for 40 days (avg yield 38 mg tissue per ml medium) a like amount (40%) of the C^{14} available in the medium was obtained in extracts. The bulk of the radioactivity was in the non-polynucleotide, soluble fraction although a substantial amount of labeling in RNA also occurred (table 1).

TABLE 1

Distribution of Radioactivity from Benzyladenine in Soybean and Tobacco Tissues

The figures represent a percent of the C^{14} taken up by the tissues as benzyladenine and are averages of 2 to 5 experiments. Each experiment involved 30 pieces of tissue, incubated from 20 to 40 days, on 250 ml of a medium containing an average of 6.763×10^6 cpm as C^{14} labeled benzyladenine. Of this amount an average of 2.75×10^6 cpm (or about 40% of that administered) were recovered by extraction from each batch of 30 pieces of tissue.

Fraction	N,6-Benzyladenine-8-C^{14}		N,6-Benzyladenine-benzyl-C^{14}	
	Tobacco	Soybean	Tobacco	Soybean
	% of total		% of total	
*Nonpolynucleotide, low molecular weight materials	84.5	84.3	98.0	98.3
Total RNA	14.7	15.0	2.0	1.7
Soluble RNA	...	...	1.6	1.5
Ribosomal RNA	...	...	0.4	0.2
DNA	0.8	0.7	<0.001	<0.001

* See text for details of extraction procedure.

Chromatography of the nonpolynucleotide fractions extracted in ethanol and other organic solvents revealed extensive metabolism of the purine moiety of the kinin. At least 9 radioactive metabolites were separated by paper chromatography of extracts of both soybean and tobacco (Fig. 1) although the bulk of the C^{14} is confined to 2 or 3 products.

It is clear (table 1) that the purine moiety of N,6-benzyladenine is

Fig. 1. Radiochromatograms of the soluble, nonpolynucleotide fraction of tobacco and soybean tissues, grown on media containing N,6-benzyladenine-8-C^{14} or N,6-benzyladenine-benzyl-C.^{14} Several of the minor radioactive spots were too faint for photographic reproduction. Solvent systems: t-butyl alcohol, glacial acetic acid, water 3:1:1, v/v (A and C); isopropanol, HCl, water (670:176:154, v/v) (B); isopropanol, NH$_4$OH, water (16:1:3, v/v) (D).

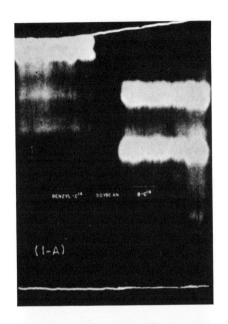

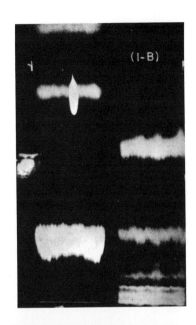

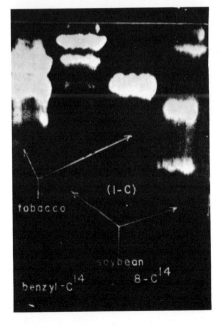

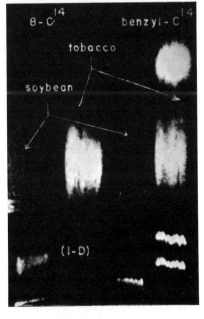

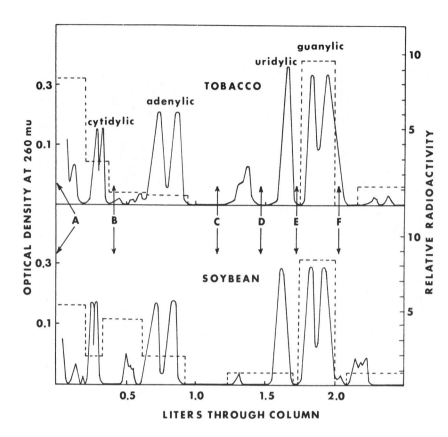

Fig. 2. Anion exchange chromatogram of KOH hydrolyzed RNA from tobacco and soybean tissues grown on $N,6$-benzyladenine-8-C^{14}. Nucleotides from about 15 g (fr wt) tissue were put on a column 1×12 cm of Dowex-1-$\times$ 8,200 to 400 mesh in formate form. The column was eluted as follows: A) 0.02 M formic acid, B) 0.15 M formic acid, C) 0.01 M formic acid + 0.05 M ammonium formate, D) 0.1 M formic acid + 0.1 M ammonium formate, E) convex gradient 0.1 M to 1.0 M formic acid + ammonium formate, F) 1.0 M formic acid + 1.0 M ammonium formate. In some runs F) was omitted without changing the results. See text for description of assay for radioactivity.

incorporated to a fairly large extent into the RNA of soybean and tobacco tissue. Anion exchange chromatography of RNA nucleotides shows that both major and minor components of the RNA are labeled with C^{14} (Fig. 2). The purine moiety of benzyladenine appeared to be incorporated into guanylic acid preferentially to adenylic acid (Fig. 2). To check this point further, KOH hydrolysates of tobacco RNA were chromatographed on Whatman No. 3 MM paper and assayed for radioactivity in a paper strip counter; again the bulk of the C^{14} was associated with guanylic acid (Fig. 3).

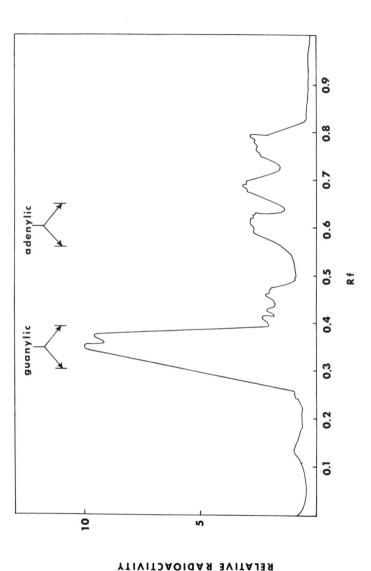

Fig. 3. Distribution of C^{14} in RNA nucleotides from tobacco tissue grown on $N,6$-benzyladenine-8-C^{14}. Nucleotides were separated by chromatography on Whatman No. 3 MM paper in isobutyric acid, water, NH_4OH, 0.1 M disodium ethylenediaminetetraacetate (100 : 55.8 : 4.2 : 1.6, v/v). Radioactivity was assayed in a Nuclear-Chicago Actigraph II paper strip counter.

Metabolism of N,6-Benzyladenine-Benzyl-C^{14}

Figure 1 demonstrates that the side chain of benzyladenine is likewise extensively metabolized. An even more striking finding is that most of the radioactive metabolites of benzyl labeled benzyladenine do not correspond in R_F values to radioactive metabolites of purine ring labeled benzyladenine. Such a finding indicates that the bulk of the kinin taken up by the tissue has been degraded. Liquid scintillation counting of paper chromatograms run in several solvent systems shows that the benzyl side chain was cleaved from the adenine moiety in more than 95% of the benzyladenine taken up by the tissue.

Since the purine nucleus of benzyladenine was incorporated into both major and minor RNA components (Fig. 2), it is important to know whether or not the benzyl side chain accompanied the entry of any of

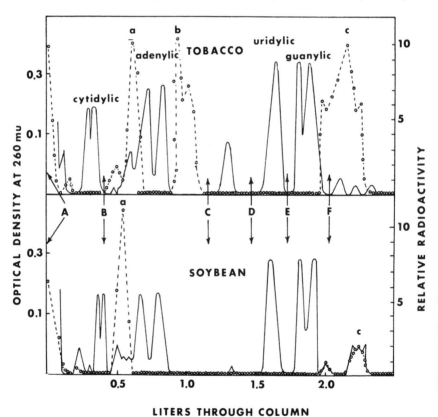

Fig. 4. Anion exchange chromatogram of KOH hydrolyzed RNA from tobacco and soybean tissues grown on N,6-benzyl-adenine-benzyl-C^{14}. See legend to Fig. 2 for fractionation procedure. See text for description of assay for radioactivity.

the purine into polynucleotides. Accordingly, KOH hydrolysates were made of exhaustively extracted tissue which had been growing on benzyl-adenine-benzyl-C^{14}, and these showed a small, but definite and repeatable, amount of radioactivity (table 1). The distribution of C^{14} in nucleotides from the KOH hydrolysate fractioned on Dowex-1 anion exchange resin is shown in Fig. 4. This procedure has been repeated several times and each fraction counted by both liquid scintillation techniques described in Materials and Methods; with the exception of minor differences due to subtle variations in technique, the general pattern of labeling shown in Fig. 4 was always obtained.

Radioactive material eluted from the column just prior to adenosine-2'-phosphate (fraction a, Fig. 4) is of particular importance since it occurs as a major radioactive peak in the RNA of both kinin requiring tissues. This fraction was taken to dryness, hydrolyzed at 100° in 1 N HCl for 90 minutes, the HCl removed with the aid of an ion-retardation resin (AG11A8, Calbiochem) and the hydrolysate co-chromatographed on Whatman No. 1 paper with benzyladenine. About 75% of the radio-activity was associated with the benzyladenine control spot in the following solvent systems: (a) water (b) t-butyl-alcohol, glacial acetic acid, water (3:1:1, v/v) (c) isopropanol, HCl, water (670:176:154, v/v) (d) isopropanol, NH_4OH, water (16:1:3,v/v). The bulk of the remainder of the C^{14} moved with R_F values in these solvent systems similar to $N,6$-methyladenine. Radioactive components b and c, especially prominent in tobacco, occur in amounts too small even to obtain ultraviolet spectra and have not been identified.

Separation of Labeled RNA into Soluble and Ribosomal Fractions

In order to determine if the observed incorporation of benzyladenine occurred preferentially into any RNA species, soluble and ribosomal fractions were obtained by differential centrifugation and purified by the method of Bergquist and Matthews [1]. In a typical experiment RNA was isolated from 29 g of tobacco tissue which had been growing for 30 days on a medium containing $N,6$-benzyladenine-benzyl-C^{14}. The combined soluble nonpolynucleotide fractions contained approximately 10^6 cpm, while the purified soluble RNA fraction contained 15,660 cpm and the ribosomal RNA 3658 cpm. A similar excess of radioactivity in the soluble RNA as compared to the ribosomal fraction was obtained in repeat runs using the differential centrifugation technique. In general the amount of C^{14} incorporated into soluble RNA varied from 0.5 to 2.5% of the C^{14} present in the nonpolynucleotide material.

As a further check on these results total cellular nucleic acids from soybean and tobacco tissues grown for 30 days on a medium containing $N,6$-benzyladenine-benzyl-C^{14} were subjected to methylated albumin

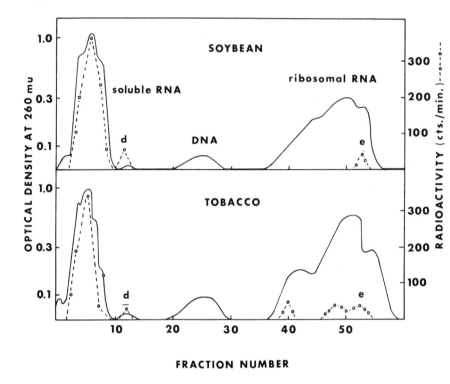

Fig. 5. Fractionation of nucleic acids from tissues growing on media containing N,6-benzyladenine-benzyl-C^{14} on methylated albumin-coated kieselguhr [13]. Nucleic acid (in 0.05 M sodium phosphate buffer, pH 6.7) was extracted by a phenol-sodium lauryl sulfate method [3] from about 10 g (fr wt) tissue, and separated on a column 2 cm in diameter having a 50 ml bed volume. The column was eluted with an NaCl gradient from 0.3 M to 1.2 M. See text for details of radioactivity assay.

chromatography. Again it is clear (Fig. 5) that the great bulk of the radioactivity is in soluble RNA although small amounts appeared in other RNA fractions. The identity of radioactive component d is not clear although a substance having similar chromatographic properties has been characterized as precursor transfer RNA [5]. The fractionation shown in Fig. 5 has been repeated 4 times with similar results.

Soluble RNA isolated on methylated albumin columns was precipitated along with unlabeled carrier RNA by adding 3 volumes of 95% ethanol in the presence of magnesium ions to the elute at pH 4.0 and allowing the mixture to stand overnight at 0°. The precipitate was collected by centrifugation, washed twice with 70% ethanol, and hydrolyzed in HCl at 100° for 90 minutes. About 50% of the radioactive material in the hydrolysates corresponded in R_F values on paper chromatograms to benzyladenine in 3 solvent systems (see for example Fig. 6). One other

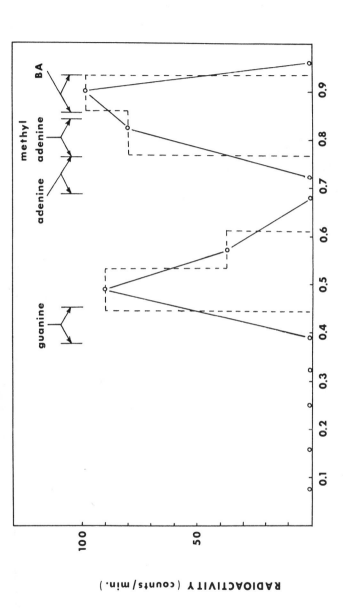

Fig. 6. Chromatographic distribution of radioactivity in an HCl hydrolysate of soluble RNA isolated from tobacco tissue grown on $N,6$-benzyl-adenine-benzyl-C^{14}. RNA was isolated by methylated albumin chromatography as shown in Fig. 5, and hydrolyzed in 1 N HCl at 100° for 90 minutes. The hydrolysate was co-chromatographed on Whatman No. 1 paper with unlabeled BA in t-butyl alcohol, glacial acetic acid, water (3:1:1, v/v). Strips were cut out and assayed for radioactivity by liquid scintillation spectrometry as described in the text. Each point is the midpoint of a strip (area of strip is designated by dotted lines).

major radioactive component was present in both soybean and tobacco soluble RNA and was clearly separated from the benzyladenine area in each of the 3 solvent systems used. The second labeled components are not the same substance in the 2 tissues, however, since their R_F values clearly differed.

Discussion

The data presented in this paper suggest that a small amount of the benzyladenine supplied to kinin requiring tissues is incorporated into soluble RNA. The most convincing evidence for this incorporation is that radioactivity appeared in RNA even when the kinin was supplied with C^{14} in the nonpurine portion (methylene carbon of the side chain) and that up to 50% of the radioactive material in soluble RNA had R_F values on paper chromatograms similar to that of benzyladenine in 3 solvent systems.

Our data do not, however, rule out the possibility that the benzyl side chain is first removed from benzyladenine and then reattached to adenine already in RNA in a manner analogous to the enzymatic methylation of RNA components, a process which is known to occur at the polynucleotide level [7]. Furthermore, the metabolism of BA-benzyl-C^{14} leading to entry of the labeled methylene carbon into the active methyl pool could account for the presence of C^{14} in the other soluble RNA components. Our studies make it appear probable that both intact BA and some of its metabolites are incorporated into soluble RNA.

The incorporation of unnatural bases presumably intact into the nucleic acids of various organisms is well established [e.g., 12] and it is not surprising to find a similar incorporation of the adenine analogue studied here. Whether or not the presence of benzyladenine in RNA is related to its biological function cannot be answered with the present study. It is instructive, however, to note that nearly all of the benzyladenine taken up is degraded by both soybean and tobacco tissues; the benzyladenine found in RNA apparently constitutes a substantial portion of the kinin remaining intact in the tissue after 20 days. It is, of course, possible that benzyladenine having fulfilled its biological role is then immediately degraded; equally likely is that one of the minor metabolic products found in the soluble nonpolynucleotide fraction is an active kinin. On the other hand the ability of kinins to promote RNA and protein synthesis in several systems [19] and the high degree of localization of kinin effects to their site of application [18, 23] suggest that kinins are rapidly incorporated into larger molecules such as RNA, a proposal first made by Thimann and Laloraya [23]. Furthermore the effectiveness at very low concentrations of the kinin, N,6-(γ,γ-dimethylallyl amino)-purine [21] and the activity of low levels of kinetin (N,6-furfurylaminopurine) itself in a kinin-requiring strain of *Clostridium thermocellum* [20] raise the possibility that the relatively high BA requirement exhibited by the tissue cultures used in this study is related to their ability to degrade much of the kinin taken up. Presumably then, only a small amount of the BA entering soybean and tobacco tissue is actually functional, perhaps as a part of soluble RNA.

There is an obvious relationship between the 6-substituted adenines which act as kinins and the methylated bases known to exist naturally in RNA. One of these, N,6-methyladenine, a naturally occurring constituent of the RNA of several organisms, has, in fact, distinct kinetin-like properties under certain circumstances [16]. Studies with N,6-methyladenine-methyl-C^{14} indicate that this kinin is likewise incorporated into the RNA of kinin-requiring soybean and tobacco tissues (unpublished data). The recent discovery that certain 1-substituted adenines are also kinins [11] bolsters the possibility that kinin action is related in some manner to that of the unusual bases in RNA.

The function of the minor components of RNA is still obscure. Recent studies of Comb and Katz [5] indicate, however, that precursor transfer RNA (t-RNA), which has an overall base composition similar to functional t-RNA but lacks methylated bases and pseudouridine, is unable to form amino acyl RNA; on the other hand it should be pointed out that earlier results by Starr [22] with methyl poor t-RNA contradict this finding. Whatever the specific function of methylated bases in RNA, it is tempting to think that the incorporation of BA into t-RNA confers amino acid transfer competency on the molecule, much as methylation may do. An interesting consequence of this line of reasoning is that those plant tissues which require kinins for in vitro growth may have lost the ability to methylate RNA; the kinin by virtue of its incorporation into RNA provides the biological equivalent of an RNA methylating enzyme. It could be visualized, therefore, that the control for the differentiation of a meristematic plant cell into a nondividing one is the switching off of genetic information for the synthesis of RNA methylating enzymes. Such an idea implies that kinins have no normal biological role in the intact plant but simply furnish an alternate method for providing substituted bases in RNA, thus stimulating in vitro growth of differentiated cells.

Although it is clear that no C^{14} from BA-benzyl-C^{14} is incorporated into tobacco and soybean DNA, the small amount of radioactivity in RNA fractions other than soluble RNA might have significance. Especially interesting is C^{14} labeled component e (Fig. 5) eluted from the methylated albumin column near the end of the ribosomal RNA fraction from both soybean and tobacco tissues; similar areas on chromatograms of peanut cotyledon nucleic acid have been described by Cherry [3] as messenger RNA. An attractive hypothesis is that kinins act as derepressing agents, perhaps by being incorporated into a particular m-RNA thereby preventing its normal repressing function. Further work is needed to discriminate between this and other equally likely possibilities.

Literature Cited

1. Bergquist, P. L. and R. E. F. Matthews. 1962. Occurrence and distribution of methylated purines in the ribonucleic acids of subcellular fractions. Biochem. J. 85: 305–13.

2. Bullock, M. N., J. J. Hand, and E. L. R. Stokstad. 1956. Synthesis of 6-substituted purines. J. Am. Chem. Soc. 78: 3693–96.

3. Cherry, J. H. 1964. Association of rapidly metabolized DNA and RNA. Science 146: 1066–69.

4. Cohn, W. E. and E. Volkin. 1951. Nucleoside-5'-phosphates from ribonucleic acid. Nature 167: 483–84.

5. Comb, D. G. and S. Katz. 1964. Studies on the biosynthesis and methylation of transfer RNA. J. Mol. Biol. 8: 790–800.

6. Daly, J. W. and B. E. Christensen. 1956. Purines. VI. The preparation of certain 6-substituted and 6,9-disubstituted purines. J. Org. Chem. 21: 177–79.

7. Fleissner, E. and E. Borek. 1962. A new enzyme of RNA synthesis: RNA methylase. Proc. Natl. Acad. Sci. U.S. 48: 1199–1203.

8. Fox, J. E. 1963. Growth factor requirements and chromosome number in tobacco tissue cultures. Physiol. Plantarum 16: 793–803.

9. Fox, J. E. 1964. Incorporation of kinins into the RNA of plant tissue cultures. Plant Physiol. 39: xxxi.

10. Fox, J. E. 1964. Indoleacetic acid-kinetin antagonism in certain tissue culture systems. Plant Cell Physiol. 5: 251–54.

11. Hamzi, Q. H. and F. Skoog. 1964. Kinetin-like growth-promoting activity of 1-substituted adenines [1-benzyl-6-amino purine and 1-(γ,γ-dimethylallyl)-6-aminopurine]. Proc. Natl. Acad. Sci. U.S. 51: 76–83.

12. Mandel, H. G., P. E. Carlo, and P. R. Smith. 1954. The incorporation of 8-azaguanine into nucleic acids of tumor-bearing mice. J. Biol. Chem. 206: 181–89.

13. Mandel, J. D. and A. D. Hershey. 1960. A fractionating column for analysis of nucleic acids. Analyt. Biochem. 1: 66–77.

14. McCalla, D. R., D. J. Morré, and D. Osborne. 1962. The metabolism of a kinin, benzyladenine. Biochem. Biophys. Acta 55: 522–28.

15. Miller, C. O. 1961. Kinetin and related compounds in plant growth. Ann. Rev. Plant Physiol. 12: 395–408.

16. Miller, C. O. 1962. Interaction of 6-methylamino-purine and adenine in division of soybean cells. Nature 194: 787–88.

17. Miller, C. O. 1961. Kinetin and kinetin-like compounds. Modern Methods of Plant Analysis. Vol VI: Springer-Verlag, Berlin. p 194–202.

18. Mothes, K., L. Engelbrecht, and O. Kulajewa. 1959. Über die Wirkung des

Kinetins auf Stickstoffverteilung und Eiweiss-synthese in isolierte Blättern. Flora (Jena). 147: 445–64.

19. Octa, Y. 1964. RNA in developing plant cells. Ann. Rev. Plant Physiol. 15: 17–36.

20. Quinn, L. Y., R. P. Oates, and T. S. Beers. 1963. Support of cellulose digestion by *Clostridium thermocellum* in a kinetin-supplemented basal medium. J. Bacteriol. 86: 1359.

21. Rogozinska, J. H., J. P. Helgeson, and F. Skoog. 1964. Tests for kinetin-like growth promoting activities of triacanthine and its isomer, 6-(γ,γ-dimethyl-allylamino)-purine. Physiol. Plantarum 17: 165–76.

22. Starr, J. L. 1963. The incorporation of amino acids into methyl-poor amino acid transfer ribonucleic acid. Biochem. Biophys. Res. Commun. 10: 181–85.

23. Thimann, K. V. and M. M. Laloraya. 1960. Changes in nitrogen in pea stem sections under the action of kinetin. Physiol. Plantarum 13: 165–78.

4 / Phytochrome and Florigen

Light regulates plant growth in a very important way quite distinct from the energy it supplies in photosynthesis. Flowering, for example, can be induced under certain conditions by little more light than is given off by a burning match. In a similar manner certain seeds are stimulated to germinate by a tiny shot of red light. Stem and leaf growth, dormancy, pigment formation, in fact most phases of plant life, are under the control of a pigment known as phytochrome, which absorbs red light.

The development of our knowledge about phytochrome has been one of the most rewarding chapters of plant physiology and biochemistry. Much of the work has been done at the United States Department of Agriculture at Beltsville, Md., and two of the men most responsible for advances in this area are the authors of the first paper in this section. In 1960 Borthwick and Hendricks summarized the state of knowledge about phytochrome and pointed the way to further studies that only now are appearing. There can be no question that during the next few years we will begin to see answers to questions such as these: How can a single pigment translate a small amount of light energy into far-reaching changes in the development of plant growth? Dare we guess that the answer will again involve the trinity of molecular biology—DNA, RNA, and protein synthesis?

To young students of plant growth it seems a very long time ago that evidence was first obtained for the formation in the leaves of plants, under the right photoperiod, of a substance that caused flowering in other parts of the plant. This hypothetical material is referred to as "florigen," and, in truth, investigators have pursued this will-o'-the-wisp for many years. The last reading in this collection, therefore, created a sensation when it appeared in 1960 with the announcement that at last an extract from flowering cocklebur plants had been obtained that could cause flowering in plants grown under noninductive day lengths. Although we do not yet have a final answer about florigen, it is clear that we must now think of this substance as a chemical that regulates an important phase of plant growth.

Photoperiodism in Plants

H. A. Borthwick
S. B. Hendricks

Flowering of plants depends upon the length of the night. Barley, wheat, and many other small grains bloom in early summer in response to short nights, while the later-maturing maize, soybeans, and chrysanthemums are induced to bloom by the longer nights of midsummer and autumn. This control of flowering is one of the methods of adaptation of species by which an unfavorable season is anticipated. It implies a time-measuring system that distinguishes between light and darkness through mediation of a pigment. Ways of finding the pigment and explanations of some of the features of seasonal response are described in this article.

First we give a partial explanation of the control mechanism, as a guide to understanding the seemingly odd methods used to find the explanation of seasonal response. The pigment, now called phytochrome, is a blue or a bluish-green protein that exists in two forms interconvertible by light, thus,

$$P_{660} \; \overset{660 \text{ m}\mu}{\underset{730 \text{ m}\mu}{\rightleftharpoons}} \; P_{730}$$

with 660 and 730 mμ the absorption maxima of the two forms. Form P_{730}, which is enzymatically active, changes in darkness to the inactive form P_{660} in the course of some hours, and the rates of the change and of the enzymatic action are essential factors in the plant's measurement of night length. The enzymatic reaction controlled by P_{730} also affects many aspects of plant growth besides flowering and results in a general control of growth by light. Phytochrome is present to the extent of about 1 part in 10 million in many plant tissues—an amount too little to give a noticeable color to leaves or stems of albino plants.

Discovery

Photoperiodism as a control of flowering was discovered in 1918 by Garner and Allard [1]. Their first observations were on a variety of tobacco induced to flower by the combination of a long night and a short day. Garner and Allard soon found the control in many kinds of seed plants and discovered that some varieties are responsive to long nights, others to short nights. At the time, these findings had a very great impact upon student of plant growth, who had widely held, without serious

Reprinted by permission of the authors and publisher from Science, 132: 1223–1228, 1960. Copyright 1960 by the American Association for the Advancement of Science.

questioning, that the seasonal controls must depend upon the obvious changes in temperature. Garner and Allard also pointed out the close similarity in seasonal responses of animals and plants and suggested, on the basis of its general features, that bird migration, too, is photoperiodically determined, as was later shown to be the case for several species.

Germination of many kinds of seeds also depends upon light through the mediation of phytochrome [2]. The need for light was recorded by Caspary in 1860 for seeds of *Bulliarda aquatica* (L.) DC. (= *Tillaea aquatica* L.) and was widely studied for many kinds of seeds in the ensuing century. In nature, the light requirement, which can be just a fraction of a second of sunlight, aids in preserving the species by insuring the prolonged dormancy of a store of seeds held in darkness through accidental covering with soil. This retention of viability by seeds is a plague to farmers and gardeners who expose them to light in cultivating, to germinate and grow as weeds.

The changes in length of stems, leaves, and other plant parts which occur in plants grown in subdued light or darkness, which are other manifestations of the action of phytochrome, must have been known to primitive man. In nature, the shoot from a deeply planted seed elongates until the food reserves are exhausted or until it reaches the surface and is exposed to light, which inhibits further lengthening. Plants growing in darkness are long and limber, but given just a little light, as from a 50-watt lamp at 1 meter for 1 second, they will be shorter and will stand upright. In 1929 Robert Bridges, the poet laureate, was moved to write in his *Testament of Beauty* [3]:

> and haply, if the seed be faln in a place of darkness
> roof'd in by men—if ther should be any ray or gleam
> how faint soe'er, 'twil crane and reach its pallid stalk
> into the crevice, pushing ev'n to disrupt the stones.

Possible interrelations of these several responses and of autumnal leaf drop, orientation of leaves in darkness, and root enlargement and bulb formation were not generally suspected, although the possibility of such interrelationships was apparent to Garner and Allard, who were also aware of many varied displays of photoperiodism in both plants and animals. Knowledge of each response was at first restricted to its occurrence among plant species and was systematized in works restricted to one type of response. Interest in possible causes for the control of growth by light was almost entirely speculative because of lack of experimental leads and of the rather natural tendency of observers to concern themselves more with the display—the flowering or the germination, for example—than with the causes. The first stirrings toward understanding actually came quite early, from findings on the dependence of etiolation upon light intensity (Batalin, 1871) and color (Vogt, 1915). By 1952, red light was known to be most effective in influencing most of the responses [4].

Action Spectra

Knowledge and understanding of the causes of the several responses have come from measurements of action spectra. The direct result is the finding that all the responses depend upon radiant energy and wavelength in the same way. Barley and cocklebur, representatives of plants requiring short or long nights, respectively, for flowering, have identical action spectra for the opposite responses of flowering in the former and inhibition of flowering in the latter. Although the control of flowering is not fully understood, these action spectra indicate that the mechanism is identical for the two types of plants. An even more surprising result is that this identity of action spectra is found in studies of control of stem lengthening and seed germination (Fig. 1) [4].

The action spectra have two parts, one for potentiating a response and the second for nullifying it [2, 5]. Radiation in the region of 540 to 695 mμ, with a maximum near 660 mμ, potentiates the flowering of barley, the germination of lettuce seeds, the enlargement of a pea leaf, the suppression of flowering in cocklebur, and the inhibition of lengthening of the pea stem. These potentiated responses are reversed before actual responses can occur by radiation in the region of 695 to 800 mμ. The reversals, which can be repeated many times, and the near identities of the action spectra for both promotion and reversal of the various responses on an *absolute* scale of incident energy, indicate an action of light that affects many aspects of plant growth.

The identity of the action spectra has several interesting corollaries. The action depends upon the extent of the interconversion of the phytochrome forms, and, in fact, the length of a bean stem can be controlled by applications of radiant energy (Fig. 2). If the light is intense and of mixed wavelength (white), like sunlight, an equilibrium at an intermediate pigment conversion is soon attained, the position depending upon the energy distribution in various spectral regions of the source but not upon the intensity. The pigment system can be driven to the same position by light from a flashlight or by full sunlight, with similar effects upon growth. Because the pigment changes form, conversion cannot be more than complete. Radiation from a red or a far-red source, which drives the interconversion toward completeness in one direction, can be counteracted by a low reversing irradiance.

At this stage of understanding, which was reached by 1952 [2, 5], the objectives of isolating the pigment and of finding its mode of action seemed attainable. Progress toward objectives of this type usually depends upon development of a bioassay. But the probability that the pig-

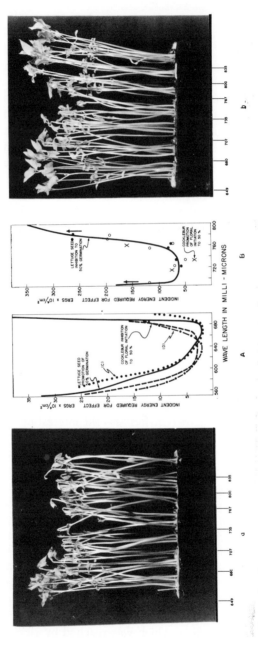

Fig. 1. Effects of radiation in the region of 560 to 850 mμ on plant growth. (a) Effects of radiation in the region of 560 to 850 mμ on stem elongation, plumular hook unfolding, and leaf expansion in dark-grown red kidney bean seedlings. (A) Action spectra for a short period of irradiation to promote germination of lettuce seeds and inhibition of floral initiation in cockleburs: (dotted curve) enhancement of elongation of a pea leaf (by 45 percent); (dot-dash curve) the promotion of flowering in barley. (B) Action spectra for inhibition of germination of lettuce seeds and enhancement of floral initiation in cockleburs. (b) Effects of irradiation on dark-grown red kidney bean seedlings under conditions similar to those of (a) except that plants were first exposed to radiation in the region of 660 mμ prior to the short exposure across the spectrum.

Fig. 2. Changes in internode lengths of pinto beans, induced at the end of the 8-hour day. The control plant on the left received no supplementary radiation. The other plants were exposed to far-red radiation for 5 minutes and then to red radiation for 0, 0.25, 0.5, 1, 2, 4, 8, and 16 minutes, respectively.

ment was a protein made reintroduction of extracts into living plant tissue seem unpromising. A more promising approach was to attempt to detect the pigment in vivo by physical methods which might be used for assay. The first approach was an attempt to obtain fluorescence of light, which can be detected at extremely low intensities, but none was found. Another approach was to search for plants with a high concentration of phytochrome, as might be evident from a blue or a bluish-green color of albino or etiolated tissue in which only small amounts of obscuring chlorophyll are present. Results again were negative, as were the results in studies to determine whether the pigment might be related to some known type of biologically active compound such as the bile pigments and the pigments of blue-green algae.

Physiological Characteristics of Phytochrome Action

Continued physiological studies were more encouraging. These indicated that the absorption coefficients of both forms of phytochrome and the relationship between their degree of interconversion and their physiological response could be found from the reversibility effect of light [6]. In a first-order reaction—indicated by a measured temperature coefficient of 1.0—the rate of change of pigment concentration $[P]$ with incident energy E (einstein units/cm^2 or 6.02×10^{23} quanta/cm^2) is

$$\frac{d[P]}{dE} = -k\ [P_0]\ (1 - F)$$

where F is the fraction of the pigment converted and is given by $F = a\, \phi\, \chi\, E_{\text{incident}}$.

In the last expression P_0 is the amount of phytochrome in a square centimeter of the test object, a is the molar absorption coefficient, ϕ is the quantum efficiency of the change, and χ is the fraction of incident light reaching the pigment. If the change is reversible, a similar first-order differential equation expresses the reverse change, and the two equations can be solved to give the degree of pigment conversion that corresponds to various degrees of physiological response and the value of $a\, \phi\, \chi$ for the two pigment forms. In this way, a was found to be of the order of 10^7 square centimeters per gram molecule for both forms of phytochrome; this means that both forms are as intensely colored as chlorophyll and most dyes.

The small degree of change (of the red-absorbing form P_{660} to P_{730}) required to produce half saturation of the stem-lengthening responses of the pinto bean and leaf lengthening of peas indicated that P_{730} is probably the physiologically active form and is an enzyme and, accordingly, a protein. That P_{730} is an enzyme had first been suspected from the fact that many seeds in which P_{660} is present can lie in the soil for years without germinating and ultimately without respiring. Exposure to light for a few seconds, which changes P_{660} to P_{730}, causes resumption of respiration and leads to germination. The facts that most seeds that require light to germinate are small, implying reserves of fat, and that one of the first evident changes in the germinating seeds is the conversion of fat to starch give additional support to the supposition that P_{730} is an enzyme and possibly one involved in fat conversion.

The requirement for light in the reddening of apples had been known for centuries to some horticulturists, who used light to deepen the color of the fruit and to apply designs with masking stencils. The effective regions of the spectrum, however, were not known even as late of 1956. Upon study, synthesis of anthocyanin, the red pigment in the apple skin and many other plant tissues, was found to take place with light in the region of 550 to 750 mμ [7, 8], although the action spectrum was not limited to this region. The amount of anthocyanin ultimately formed was linearly dependent upon the radiant energy after an induction period of one or two hours. In several objects (milo seedlings, for example) formation of anthocyanin can be reversibly controlled for several hours after being potentiated. The action spectrum for the reversal is identical with that for photoperiodism, and the energy requirements for half conversion of phytochrome and for the reversal are also identical. The high energy requirement for the initial potentiation, however, could not be explained until the action spectrum was found to depend upon a combination of the absorption spectra of the two forms of phytochrome in the spectral region where both forms absorb, as is particularly evident for red cabbage seedlings (Fig. 3) [7]. From this knowledge the concentration of phytochrome in the seedlings could be estimated; it was found to be of the order of $10^{-7}M$ in a favorable object. It was possible to make the estimate because the anthocyanin formed by the action of a measured amount of incident radiation could be extracted and the amount (in gram molecules) established by analysis.

Detection of Phytochrome by Differential Spectrophotometry

It was a logical and intuitive conclusion from the experimental observations upon growth, germination, and flowering that phytochrome could be detected in tissue by "adequately" sensitive spectroscopic methods. The difficulty, however, was with "adequately," for the method would have to be sensitive to a change in the light transmitted by the tissue of the order of one part of the incident light in 10^6 parts, and it would have to be applicable to highly scattering media. K. H. Norris and his associates, of the Agricultural Marketing Service, U.S. Department of Agri-

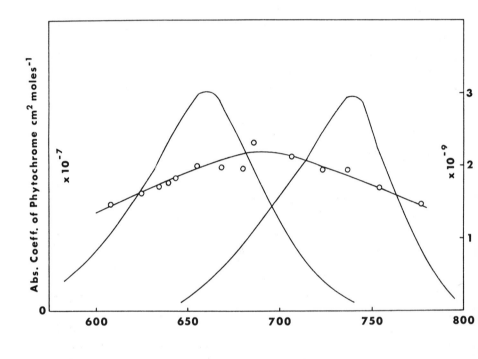

Fig. 3. Variations with wavelength of molecular extinctions of the two forms of phytochrome and the action spectrum for the formation of anthocyanin in red cabbage.

culture, designed and built a simple differential spectrometer having the required sensitivity, for use in measuring the ripening of fruits [9]. The instrument is similar in principle to the double-beam differential spectrometer developed by Chance [10] for following the changes of respiratory pigments in living tissue. Through use of the instrument of Norris *et al.*, values of Δ in Δ (Δ O.D.) = [(O.D.$_{660}$ − O.D.$_{730}$) after irradiation in the region of 660 mμ] − [(O.D.$_{660}$ − O.D.$_{730}$) after irradiation in the region of 730 mμ] can be obtained as phytochrome is changed from P_{660} to P_{730} or from P_{730} to P_{660} [11]. An adequately stable single-beam spectrophotometer suitable for use with highly scattering media also was available. The change in optical density in shoots of dark-grown seedlings of maize with wavelength of light as phytochrome is changed in form is shown in Fig. 4*a* [11]. This curve reflects the features evident in the several action spectra for control of growth (Fig. 1).

We now had the desired assay method for phytochrome, provided the reversibility with light was effective on broken tissue. Fortunately, clear aqueous solutions of extracted nonparticulate cytoplasm of etiolated maize responded reversibly. Protein fractions salted out of the aqueous extracts contained the reversible pigment. The concentration of phytochrome has now been increased to more than 20 times that of the first extract by H. W. Siegelman, who used methods of protein chemistry.

The differential spectroscopic method can be used directly for estimating the concentration of phytochrome in living tissue having low chlorophyll concentrations. Phytochrome is detectable, for example, in cauliflower and artichoke florets, in avocado and Zucchini squash fruits, and in etiolated tissue of many seedlings of grasses and cotyledons of several members of the cabbage family. It has been detected in extracts of spinach leaves, but the reversible change was not detected in extracts of cocklebur and soybean leaves known to be photoperiodically responsive.

The separated phytochrome is the active principle of photoperiodism and related plant-growth phenomena controlled by light. The properties in solution are those foretold by the physiological responses. In solution, however, neither P_{660} nor P_{730} undergoes spontaneous change to the other form. As would be anticipated, the extracts, even though photoreversible, apparently lack some of the factors necessary for the enzymatic activity of P_{730} with which its reversal in darkness to P_{660} is associated.

The entry of phytochrome into so many aspects of plant growth indicates that P_{730} is an enzyme for a reaction common to many reaction sequences in plants. In a sense, it may control a "bottleneck" through which much of the material for plant growth must pass. Several clues as to the region of action are evident from effects upon seed germination and anthocyanin synthesis, but a further one is most telling. Apple skins produce ethanol in darkness from sucrose as a substrate [12]. The ethanol production is stopped by light of high intensity, with the accompanying formation of the red anthocyanin of the skin. This indicates that the essential light reaction controls the fate of a two- or three-carbon compound, permitting its passage either to ethanol or, through condensation, to an aromatic compound.

A reasonable, but entirely speculative concept, is that the reaction is

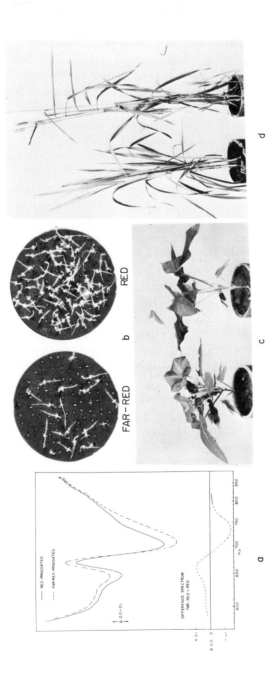

Fig. 4. (a) Recorded optical densities from corn shoots after red and far-red irradiations as a function of wavelength (in millimicrons). The difference spectrum is shown at bottom. (b, c, d) Growth responses to far-red and red radiation: (b) Germination of lettuce seeds is promoted by red radiation; (c) flowering of the short-day morning-glory plant is influenced oppositely to flowering of (d) long-day wheat plant.

closely associated with reactions of acyl coenzyme A compounds which are known to be essential for fat utilization and formation (seed germination), the operation of the Krebs cycle, and anthocyanin and sterol syntheses. In fact, regulation of acetyl coenzyme A levels is an ideal control for growth because more than three-fourths of the carbon of a plant is incorporated in acetyl coenzyme A at some stage of passage [13]. The purpose of these comments, which are speculative, is to indicate that a single specific type of reaction, not too difficult to demonstrate experimentally, can well lead to the many spectacular displays of growth control by light.

Time Measurement

The way in which plants measure time in darkness can now be outlined. Essential to the discussion is the fact that, in plants irradiated with red light at the onset of darkness to change any P_{660} present to P_{730}, the phytochrome reverts to the P_{660} form within 4 hours of darkness. In the several plants upon which measurements were made, either physiologically by following flowering or physically from the change in light absorption, reversion of P_{730} to P_{660} has a half-life of about 2 hours. If the half-life is constant, P_{730} will be reduced to $(\frac{1}{2})^5$, or to 3.1 percent, of its initial activity after 10 hours in darkness. This is the approximate critical length of night for control of flowering of plants requiring either long or short nights for induction.

While change of P_{730} to P_{660} in darkness is essential for flowering of photoperiodically responsive plants, it is not the only controlling factor. The metabolic reserves also are time-dependent. These reserves are built up as simple sugars, polysaccharides, starch, and fatty acids through photosynthesis during the day and are utilized at night in systems of reactions, including those controlled by the P_{730} form of phytochrome. In short, the decreasing amount of P_{730} depends for action upon reserves that decrease with time.

Endogenous rhythms are a third pertinent feature of change in plants and animals during darkness. These rhythmic changes have been studied extensively by E. Bunning, of the University of Tübingen, who has implicated them in the timing of photoperiodism [14, 15]. They have been the subject of a recent symposium on "Biological Clocks" [16], in which their importance for time sensing by animals was emphasized. A feature of an interconnected system, be it mechanical, hydraulic, electrical, financial, or biochemical, is that a disturbance of input tends to produce oscillations of the output. The frequencies of the oscillations depend upon coupling constants of the system and the degree of entrainment by the disturbance.

The rhythms of biological objects, which are referred to as "circadian" rhythms, generally complete a cycle in about 24 hours. This cycle length is indicative of the evolutionary origin of the process, locking together the rhythm and the change of day and night. The activity cycles of animals in continuous darkness indicate that the periods of the cycle are endogenous, or "free-running" [15]. The degree to which the rhythms are "free-running" in plants, however, is difficult to assess.

In plants, the initial disturbances upon entering darkness are so great and the times of marked change are such large fractions of the dark period as to cause entrainment of endogenous periods. Only after the entrainment is lessened can the endogenous rhythm be clearly evident. Data on periodic leaf movement and flowering control in long periods of darkness suggest that this lessening of the initial disturbances reaches critical values only after about 16 hours, a period longer than the natural night in regions where most plants grow.

Another finding, the significance of which is by no means clear, is that photoreversibility of flowering is lost within less than an hour after change of P_{660} to P_{730} near the middle of normal dark periods effective for the control of flowering. In extreme cases, illustrated by the flowering of lamb's-quarters and young Japanese morning-glory plants [17], radiation in the region of 660 mμ is effective in producing a response which is not reversed by radiation in the region of 730 mμ. The suggestion is that conversion of P_{730} is quenched, possibly by association with the substrate upon which it acts enzymatically and to which energy is transferred in the course of anthocyanin synthesis.

Temperature changes in the environment also influence many aspects of plant growth, as has been emphasized in particular by F. W. Went of the Missouri Botanical Garden [18]. That all components of change in an interconnected system should be temperature-dependent is expected. The change in output, however, can be compensated by interconnections of components to achieve an approximate constancy, once the transient of initial change has passed. This is in accord with both the slight change of endogenous rhythms with temperature and the induction of many growth responses by temperature change. An illustration of the control is afforded by the germination of many seeds which require both variation of temperature and exposure to light.

The emphasis placed on the reasons for responses to light has diverted attention from many displays of photoperiodism and striking controls of growth. One of the displays is the dormancy of terminal buds of trees and other woody plants, which affects annual growth and eventual form. The cessation of growth is usually induced by long nights. It can sometimes be broken by a return to short nights but often requires removal of leaves and a period of low temperatures. These features of change within the plant can be understood as synchronization with the seasonal change of the environment in temperature and length of night.

Animals also are photoperiodic for reproduction, migration, and dormancy. Comparisons of descriptive aspects of photoperiodism in plants and animals show many striking similarities. Some workers hold that endogenous rhythms are the basic common causative feature. In keeping with the developments discussed above, however, the working hypothesis is that a common reaction may underlie the endogenous rhythms and the photoperiodic responses. A need exists both for many more studies of plants and for studies of cause rather than display in animals. Even if causes for plants and animals prove to be unrelated, it would be interesting to find in what ways similar ends are achieved.

References

1. W. W. Garner and H. A. Allard, *J. Agr. Research* **18**, 553 (1920).

2. H. A. Borthwick, S. B. Hendricks, M. W. Parker, E. H. Toole, V. K. Toole, *Proc. Natl. Acad. Sci. U.S.* **38**, 662 (1952).

3. R. Bridges, *The Testament of Beauty* (Oxford Univ. Press, 1929), p. 43 (quoted with permission of the Oxford University Press).

4. S. B. Hendricks and H. A. Borthwick, in *Aspects of Synthesis in Order and Growth*, D. Rudnick, Ed. (Princeton Univ. Press, Princeton, N.J., 1954).

5. H. A. Borthwick, S. B. Hendricks, M. W. Parker, *Proc. Natl. Acad. Sci. U.S.* **38**, 929 (1952).

6. S. B. Hendricks, H. A. Borthwick, R. J. Downs, *ibid.* **42**, 19 (1956).

7. H. W. Siegelman and S. B. Hendricks, *Plant Physiol.* **32**, 393 (1957).

8. ———, *ibid.* **33**, 185 (1958).

9. G. S. Birth, *Agr. Eng.*, in press.

10. B. Chance, in *Methods of Enzymology*, S. P. Colowick and N. O. Kaplan, Eds. (Academic Press, New York, 1957), vol. 4.

11. W. L. Butler, K. H. Norris, H. W. Siegelman, S. B. Hendricks, *Proc. Natl. Acad. Sci. U.S.* **45**, 1703 (1959).

12. H. W. Siegelman and S. B. Hendricks, *Plant Physiol.* **33**, 409 (1958).

13. H. A. Krebs and H. L. Kornberg, *Ergeb. Physiol.* **49**, 212 (1957).

14. E. Bunning, *Jahrb. wiss. Botan.* **75**, 439 (1931).

15. ———, *Die Physiologische Uhr* (Springer, Berlin, 1958).

16. "Biological Clocks," paper presented at the Cold Spring Harbor Symposium on Quantitative Biology (1960).

17. S. Nakayama, H. A. Borthwick, S. B. Hendricks, *Botan. Gaz.*, in press.

18. F. W. Went, in *Vernalization and Photoperiodism*, A. E. Murneek and R. O. Whyte, Eds. (Chronica Botanica, Waltham, Mass., 1948) [vol. 1 of *Lotsye Biological Miscellany*].

Preparation of a Floral
Initiating Extract from Xanthium

Richard G. Lincoln
Darwin L. Mayfield
Alan Cunningham

Hamner and Bonner [1] have submitted the first evidence of a hormone formed in *Xanthium* at the site of photoperiodic perception, the leaf, and later utilized by the bud in the transition from the vegetative to the flowering condition. They also record attempts to find a floral initiating preparation in extracts from flowering plant material. At the same time they tested numerous chemicals for activity. Although they did occasionally find evidence of floral-initiating activity in their plant extracts, they were unable to demonstrate any consistent pattern or to repeat their results with any confidence.

Since that time there have been occasional published reports of preparations exhibiting floral-initiating properties. Such reports have not met the test of consistent repetition, with the exception of the now well-known effect of gibberellic acid in stimulating floral development in many long-day photoperiodically sensitive plants. Lang [2] suggests that gibberellic acid is probably not the primary floral-initiating stimulus, but that it acts indirectly in stimulating flowering. The action of gibberellic acid in promoting more rapid flowering in *Xanthium* [3] also appears to be an indirect effect.

The experiment described in the present report is the last of four successful demonstrations of floral initiation in *Xanthium* plants resulting from applications of as yet unknown substance(s) extracted from the branch parts of flowering plants. Our preparation has been independently checked by B. H. Carpenter and K. C. Hamner [4], and the results are in accord with our own.

Flowering branch tips were harvested from indigenous *Xanthium strumarium* L. var. *canadense* (Mill.) T. and G. [5] of the Long Beach area. The plants were picked when the staminate terminal inflorescence was from $\frac{1}{2}$ to 1 cm in diameter. Each branch carried three to five mature leaves. The fresh material was frozen in liquid nitrogen and broken into fine fragments while in the frozen state. Care was taken that the material remained frozen until it had been thoroughly dried in a laboratory vacuum lyophilizer. After lyophilization, the material was placed in sealed containers and stored in a deep freeze at $-20°C$.

The lyophilized material was extracted with absolute methanol under

Reprinted by permission of the authors and publisher from *Science*, *133*: 756–757, 1960. Copyright 1960 by the American Association for the Advancement of Science. This work was supported by National Science Foundation Grants 7252 and 11482.

a partial vacuum sufficient to maintain the temperature of boiling methanol between −5° and −10°C. A modified Soxhlet apparatus was used with a condenser containing a dry ice-acetone slurry as a coolant. The methanol solvent was removed from the extract by evaporation at room temperature or below in a Rinco apparatus attached to a water aspirator system. The product was a dark green, tarry residue which was mixed to homogeneity with anhydrous (USP) lanolin.

Two grams of the residue mixed with 17 g of lanolin was applied to the underside of the leaf surface of ten test plants. Ten control plants were treated in like fashion with 17 g of pure lanolin. During the 14 days sub-

TABLE 1

Flowering Response of *Xanthium* After Application
of Extract

Flowering Response	Numerical Av. of Flowering Response [6]
Untreated control plants	
All ten plants vegetative	0.0
Extract-treated plants	
Five plants vegetative (one plant, stage one; two plants, stage two; two plants, stage three)	1.1

sequent to the application of the lanolin preparations, all test plants and control plants were maintained on a precise 8-hour dark and 16-hour (500 ft-ca intensity) light regime. On the 14th day after application, the terminal bud of each plant was dissected to ascertain the flowering response. The flowering stages were numerically evaluated [6], and the results are presented in Table 1. Three earlier experiments had yielded essentially similar results.

It is our belief that these results constitute the first reproducible demonstrations of floral initiation in a short-day plant as the direct result of an extract prepared from the tissues of flowering plants. It is suggested that this is a crude extract of the flowering stimulus. Currently, efforts are being directed toward further concentration and characterization of the active entity in this extract.

References and Notes

1. K. C. Hamner and J. Bonner, *Botan. Gaz.* **100**, 388 (1938).
2. A. Lang, *Proc. Natl. Acad. Sci. U.S.* **43**, 709 (1957).

3. R. G. Lincoln and K. C. Hamner, *Plant Physiol.* 33, 101 (1958).

4. A preparation of 2 g of extract mixed in 17 g of lanolin was given to B. H. Carpenter and K. C. Hamner, Botany Department, University of California, Los Angeles. The mixture was applied to ten test plants of *Xanthium;* ten comparable plants served as controls. All plants were maintained on long-day conditions for 17 days, after which they were dissected. The treated plants were flowering at the 50-percent level. All controls were vegetative.

5. C. L. Hitchcock, A. Cronquist, M. Ownbey, J. W. Thompson, *Vascular Plants of the Pacific Northwest* (Univ. of Washington Press, Seattle, 1955), part 5.

6. Results were evaluated in accordance with a numerical scale based on the diameter and morphological stage of development of the terminal staminate inflorescence. Vegetative plants were rated as zero on the scale. The first morphological change in the stem apex that could be clearly recognized as flowering was assigned a value of 1.0. A flowering apex measuring 0.25 mm in diameter was evaluated as 2.0. An additional increment of 1.0 was allowed for each 0.25 mm increase in the diameter of the developing inflorescence.